Trace Element Geochemistry in Health and Disease

Edited by Jacob Freedman

**THE
GEOLOGICAL SOCIETY
OF AMERICA**

SPECIAL PAPER 155

Trace Element Geochemistry
in Health and Disease

Edited by Jacob Freedman

**THE
GEOLOGICAL SOCIETY
OF AMERICA**

SPECIAL PAPER 155

Published by
THE GEOLOGICAL SOCIETY OF AMERICA, INC.
3300 Penrose Place
Boulder, Colorado 80301

Printed in The United States of America

*The Special Paper series was originally made possible
through the bequest of
Richard Alexander Fullerton Penrose, Jr.*

Contents

Foreword . . . . *Jacob Freedman*   vii

Geochemical environment related to health and disease . . . . . *Howard C. Hopps*   1

   References cited   7

   General references   8

Man's effect on the geochemistry of lake and stream sediments from southern
Ontario . . . . *John A. C. Fortescue and J. Terasmae*   9

   Abstract   9

   Introduction   9

   Survey planning   10

   Methods   13

   Results   13

   Discussion   16

   Conclusions   24

   References cited   25

Some possible relationships of water and soil chemistry to cardiovascular diseases
in Indiana . . . . *Ronald W. Klusman and Herbert I. Sauer*   27

   Abstract   27

   Introduction   28

   Area of study   29

   Relationship of health and environmental influences   30

   Regression analysis and Spearman rank correlation of environmental influences   36

   Summary   39

   References cited   40

Multivariate relationships between soil composition and human mortality rates in
Missouri . . . . *Ronald R. Tidball and Herbert I. Sauer*   41

   Abstract   41

   Soil—A poor measure of premature human mortality   42

   Soils and epidemiology   45

   Mortality rates   48

   Soil materials   48

   Chemical analysis of soils   49

   Distribution of county means   49

   Stepwise multiple regression   51

   New directions   55

   Acknowledgments   56

   References cited   57

The molybdenum project: Geochemical aspects . . . .
. . . . *Donald D. Runnells, Willard R. Chappell, and Robert Meglen*   61

   Abstract   61

   Introduction   62

Geochemistry   65
Comparative studies in Colorado   66
Concentrations of molybdenum below Climax mill   68
Analytical methods   69
Summary   71
Acknowledgment   71
References cited   71
Cadmium-zinc interactions: Implications for health . . . .
. . . . *Harold H. Sandstead and Leslie M. Klevay*   73
Introduction   73
Zinc and cadmium in the environment   73
Entry of cadmium into man   74
Relationship of dietary zinc and dietary cadmium   76
Zinc and cadmium interactions in the body   77
References cited   79
Therapies for environmental element deficiencies and toxic excesses . . . .
. . . . . *William H. Strain, Walter J. Pories, Edward G. Mansour, and Arthur Flynn*   83
Abstract   83
Introduction   83
Geography of death   84
Soils   88
Domestic animals   89
Man   90
Iodine   91
Iron   97
Fluorine   100
Summary   102
References cited   102
Sampling designs in environmental geochemistry . . . .
. . . . *Harry A. Tourtelot and A. T. Miesch*   107
Abstract   107
Introduction   108
Experimental designs   108
References cited   117

Foreword

Special Paper 155 includes the published papers presented at the symposium on "Trace Element Geochemistry in Health and Disease" held at the Annual Meeting of the Geological Society of America, Minneapolis, Minnesota, November 15, 1972, under the sponsorship of the Joint Technical Paper Committee of the Geological Society of America and the National Association of Geology Teachers. The first symposium on "Environmental Geochemistry in Relation to Human Health and Disease" was held in 1968 in Dallas, Texas, at the annual meeting of the American Association for the Advancement of Science and is published in Memoir 123 (1971) of the Geological Society of America.

One paper presented at the symposium in Minneapolis, "The Chemical Behavior of Major and Minor Elements in Aquatic Environments at the Earth's Surface" by R. C. Reynolds, is not included in Special Paper 155; an additional paper, "Some Possible Relationships of Water and Soil Chemistry to Cardiovascular Diseases in Indiana" by R. W. Klusman and H. I. Sauer, is included.

Among others, the following symposia and conferences on trace elements and health have contributed additional data: *Trace Substances in Environmental Health, I-VIII*, D. D. Hemphill, editor, 1968 to 1975, proceedings of the annual conferences of the University of Missouri; *Trace Element Metabolism in Animals (TEMA)—I*, edited by C. F. Mills and published by E. and S. Livingstone, Edinburgh and London, 1970; *TEMA—II*, edited by W. G. Hoekstra and others, held in Madison, Wisconsin, and sponsored by the University of Wisconsin Madison and the United States Department of Agriculture; *Geochemical Environment in Relation to Health and Disease*, edited by H. C. Hopps and H. L. Cannon, Volume 99, Annals of the New York Academy of Sciences, 1972.

The purposes of the symposia and conferences show a progressive change from revealing that the chemistry of natural materials in a geographic area is related to animal and human diseases; to effects of the geochemical environment on the health of living things and how these effects came about; to the interaction of trace elements, therapies for environmental deficiencies and toxic excesses, more detailed statewide studies of the impact of trace elements, and sample designs to minimize cost and effort. For the future, there is a need for intensive multidisciplinary studies of optimal requirements and availabilities of trace elements for man. Another major study, long overdue, should be on means of getting available information on trace elements used, as it is for plants and animals, for the benefit of mankind.

JACOB FREEDMAN

Department of Geology
Franklin and Marshall College
Lancaster, Pennsylvania 17604

Geological Society of America
Special Paper 155
© 1975

Geochemical Environment Related to Health and Disease

Howard C. Hopps
Department of Pathology, School of Medicine
University of Missouri
Columbia, Missouri 65201

Some of the relationships between geochemical environment and health and disease are well documented; for example, deficiency of iodine in soil and water and dysfunction of the thyroid gland—goiter and hypothyroidism in the adult, cretinism in the infant-child, and increased risk of thyroid cancer.

Recent evidence suggests that those relationships we know about are but the tip of the iceberg, and that geochemical environment has a profound influence on the level of health of human beings and other animals; moreover, the geochemical environment, particularly as it affects intake and utilization of trace elements, plays a major causal role in many specific diseases.

There is urgent need for a *multidisciplinary approach* to the important problem of identifying and characterizing relationships between geochemical environment and health and disease, because this problem is so complex that it cannot be resolved by geochemists, agronomists, toxicologists, nutritionists, epidemiologists, or pathologists working alone.

Because I am a pathologist—and one particularly interested in geographic pathology—my approach to this problem is by examining the geographic patterns of disease with respect to the geochemical environment in which they occur, at the same time looking at the cause(s) and mechanism of development (pathogenesis) of those diseases in which there is reason to suspect that geochemical environment may play a causal role. With this approach, disease patterns must be considered not merely in terms of incidence or prevalence of the disease, but also in terms of variations in its character: whether it is acute or chronic, mild or severe, affecting one organ or many, and so forth. Levels of health are also influenced by geochemical environment, but that shall not be considered here.

In our consideration of disease, it is essential that we recognize the *multiple causality* of most diseases (Hopps and Cuffey, 1969; Hopps, 1971). It is this requirement of multiple causal factors that is reflected in the distinctive geographic patterns of many diseases. Admittedly, genetic factors do influence this geographic

1

distribution, but from a pragmatic viewpoint, environmental factors are more important because they can be identified, characterized, and controlled more effectively. In this context of environmental causes of disease, there has been greatly intensified interest and activity in geochemical factors during the past several years.

Some of the events that testify to this increasing concern are the following: In 1969 the National Academy of Science established a subcommittee (of its National Committee for Geochemistry) on the geochemical environment related to health and disease; three monographs have been published on this general subject (Cannon and Hopps, 1971; Hopps and Cannon, 1972; Cannon and Hopps, 1972); three week-long workshops on geochemical environment related to health and disease have been held under auspices of the NAS subcommittee (proceedings of first workshop have been published by the National Academy of Sciences, 1974d—the others will be published); and a new organization, The Society for Environmental Geochemistry and Health, has been formed. These activities underscore the important health/disease effects of elements as they occur naturally in the geologic substrate, affecting the characteristics of waters and soils and, through these means, entering into the food chain to exert their influence on plants, animals, and man. Man is in a particularly adventitious position because he is high on the food pyramid, and thus he capitalizes on the fact that the plants and animals he consumes have accumulated many of the essential elements in proper amounts (Fig. 1). At the same time, man is also highly vulnerable because he may consume toxic amounts of elements (for example, mercury) that have become concentrated as a result of their passage along the food chain.

Emphasis on the harmful effects of trace elements such as mercury, lead, cadmium, and beryllium has lead many to associate them with pollution and to cast them in the role of the villain. Looking at them from another viewpoint, however, they emerge as "Metals of Life"—the term used by Williams (1971) in his excellent book of that name. And it is the metals of life on which I shall concentrate. Knowledge gained during the past decade about the number and importance of metallo-enzymes (Williams, 1971) has carried the message that trace elements are more important to health than was generally realized.[1] But this implication was not accepted in an effective way by molecular biologists, who were more concerned with individual metallo-enzymes as ends in themselves than as the means of contributing functions essential to the total system. This illustrates once again how badly we need the broad perspective that can come only from the integrated efforts of specialists. If they can be persuaded to work together, they can create a whole that is much more than the sum of its parts. Without such perspective, we shall continue to miss the forest for the trees on many important occasions.

The essentiality of some of the trace elements is evident from those obvious diseases that occur under conditions of natural deficiency, as mentioned above. At a less obvious level, other trace elements can be shown to produce significant

---

[1]The mere identification of a particular element in a metallo-enzyme is not sufficient basis to consider that element essential, because other elements may substitute or alternative metabolic pathways may exist that allow the organism to function with no significant disadvantage.

disorders when deficiency is induced under controlled laboratory conditions.

Another group of trace elements falls in the borderline region because of the extent and quality of effects that result from their deficiency—and even these effects often occur only under artificial laboratory conditions. Whether or not they should be called "essential" hinges on one's definition of the word, which, in the gray zone we are considering, depends upon one's philosophy. "Essential for continued life" offers no problem, nor does "essential to prevent overt disease." The trouble comes from a contention by some that if a trace element contributes to *optimal* health—as measured by rate of growth, bone density, reproductive capability, and so forth—it is essential. What is optimal? Is larger necessarily better? If this were true, almost all of us would be deficient in anterior pituitary hormone because amounts larger than usual (normal?) can produce individuals taller than 8 ft. Using the same set of standards, perhaps most of us should be getting less oxygen, because persons living at high elevations have hemoglobin values considerably greater than is "normal" at sea level, and an even greater (proportionate) increase in their total red blood-cell mass.

Regardless of how we define "essential," however, our interest in trace elements should go beyond deficiency *disease;* we need to be concerned about optimal *health,* which includes the ability to withstand stress, at all ages.

Some of the important functional impairments we now think of as the natural consequences of old age may, in fact, be manifestations of trace-element deficiency, excess, or imbalance and, thus, are preventable.

There is good evidence that 14 trace elements are essential for human beings:

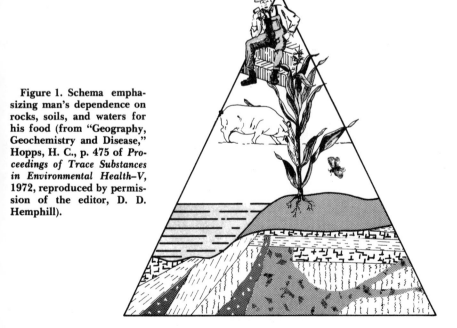

Figure 1. Schema emphasizing man's dependence on rocks, soils, and waters for his food (from "Geography, Geochemistry and Disease," Hopps, H. C., p. 475 of *Proceedings of Trace Substances in Environmental Health–V,* 1972, reproduced by permission of the editor, D. D. Hemphill).

fluorine, silicon*, vanadium*, chromium, manganese, iron, cobalt, nickel*, copper, zinc, selenium, molybdenum, tin*, and iodine. Essentiality of four of these (*) has been recognized only during the past three years, which indicates the rate at which our knowledge is expanding in this fast-moving field. (Mertz's 1972 review is an excellent general account of human requirements of trace elements to meet optimal as well as basic needs.) Merely knowing that we must have these trace elements, however, is not enough; we must get them in the right amounts—and here the geochemical environment is an important consideration.

Trace elements of the geochemical environment may reach man directly through the water that he drinks. More often, however, they take a long, often tortuous course. Figure 2 considers some of the factors involved in this course and also the factors that affect the biologic action of trace elements once they reach man.

To evaluate properly the biologic effects of trace elements once they have reached man requires that a differentiation be made between physiologic, therapeutic, and toxic levels of intake. Depending on the amount received, the effects often differ qualitatively as well as quantitatively. Because of this, one must be wary of extrapolating. For example, lithium has a favorable therapeutic effect on patients with manic manifestations and is a standard medication for such conditions. But this fact, in itself, does not warrant the assumption that *physiologic* doses of lithium act to maintain mental health. Taken therapeutically, the usual daily maintenance dosage of Li_2CO_3 contains approximately 330 milligrams of lithium; the usual intake of lithium under natural (physiologic) conditions is a mere 100 or so *micrograms* (Hamilton and Minski, 1972).

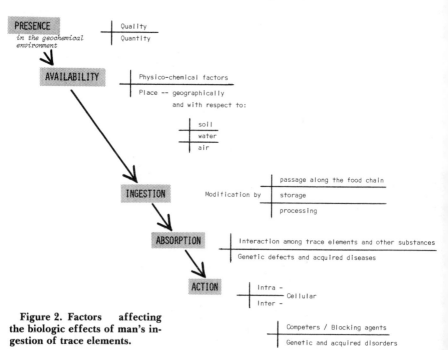

Figure 2. Factors affecting the biologic effects of man's ingestion of trace elements.

In addition to amount of intake and its chemical form, one must also consider *who* is getting the trace element *when* and *under what circumstances*. As to who, there are great variations related to species differences. For example, excess of selenium causes degeneration and fibrosis of the pancreas in poultry, produces degenerative muscle disease in ruminants, acts as a hepatotoxin in swine, and leads to cataract formation in rats. Human beings, in contrast, seem to be quite tolerant to amounts of selenium that cause serious defects in other species, except for predisposition to dental caries.

Marked variation in reaction to trace elements is also frequent within a given species. A dramatic example is observed in the response of human beings to copper. Normal individuals are tolerant to both low and high levels of copper, levels that would produce overt disease in sheep. As a result, both copper deficiency and copper toxicity disease are uncommon in man, except for the rare individual with a particular genetic disorder that seriously interferes with his normal metabolic processing of Cu. These unfortunates, even on diets low in Cu, accumulate large amounts of the element in many of their tissues and organs, particularly the liver and brain. This leads to profound dysfunction termed hepatolenticular degeneration, a condition commonly known as Wilson's disease.

The *when* is primarily concerned with the individual's stage of life, although there are variations related to seasons and other times as well. The four principal stages are those in which the dominant activities are, respectively, development, growth, maintenance, and senescence. As a rule, larger quantities of essential trace elements are required during stages of development, growth, and senescence. These three stages, occurring in early and late life, are also periods of increased susceptibility to potentially toxic trace elements.

The *under what circumstances* is more complex, because one must consider the effects of many kinds of interaction: for example, selenium and vitamin E, which, to a degree, substitute for each other; zinc and phytates (phytates, particularly in association with considerable Ca, react with Zn to interfere with its absorption from the intestinal tract); molybdenum and copper (Mo in the diet considerably increases the requirement for Cu, especially in ruminants). Figure 3 shows schematically the relationship between Cu and Mo and the effects of sulfate and tungsten on this relationship. Thus, many of the essential trace elements must be considered together with certain other elements and (or) simple chemical

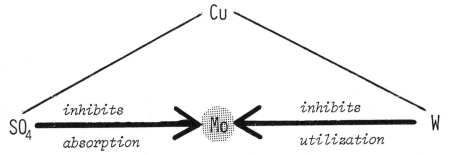

Figure 3. Schematic representation of how most trace elements (for example, molybdenum) are affected by complex interactions that control their biologic effects.

compounds to acquire an insight into the basis for the observed biologic effects.

Our relationship with our environment is a dynamic situation, and it is important to recognize that stress situations occur frequently and can greatly alter the individual's trace-element requirements: Wound healing and repair of fractures require increased amounts of zinc (Strain, 1975); regeneration of blood, to compensate for hemorrhage, requires increased amounts of iron (Hopps, 1972). There are physiologic stress situations as well as pathologic ones. For example, during the latter part of pregnancy, a woman requires approximately seven times more iron than her male counterpart (Hopps, 1972). It is likely that conditions such as atherosclerosis, hypertension, cancer, and a variety of infectious diseases increase our needs for specific trace elements, but we know relatively little about this (Hopps and Cannon, 1972).

Because this is a conceptual approach to the relationships of geochemical environment to health and disease, it is not appropriate to consider in detail the functions of each of the 14 essential trace elements that have been listed. It does seem pertinent, however, to mention some of the elements that are of particular interest today with respect to human health. This is done primarily to indicate ". . . the imminence of so much as yet unknown."

Selenium excess, as well as deficiency, has long been known to cause important effects in livestock, but not in man. There is now evidence (mainly epidemiologic) suggesting that selenium, at appropriate levels, may act to reduce the risk of cancer in human beings as well as in other animals (Pories and others, 1972; National Academy of Sciences, 1971).

Fluorine may have a favorable effect not only in protection from dental caries, but also in protection from osteoporosis (Anonymous, 1972; National Academy of Sciences, 1974b).

Chromium seems clearly related to the glucose tolerance factor, and chromium deficiency may well be one causal factor in some cases of diabetes mellitus (National Academy of Sciences, 1974a).

Zinc, required for growth and the repair/regeneration of tissues, may, under conditions of induced acute deficiency, prove useful in retarding the growth of human cancer (Pories and others, 1972).

Silicon, one of the most exciting of the "new" trace elements, may play an important role in the aging process. Its requirement in calcification and in bone and cartilage formation has been established (Carlisle, 1974).

Vanadium and **tin** are each necessary for growth of certain animal species, as determined under experimental laboratory-induced deficiency (National Academy of Sciences, 1974c; Hopkins and Mohr, 1974; Schwarz, 1974). It is not yet known what contribution they make to the health of man under natural conditions.

Nickel is another one of the "new" essential trace elements that, as yet, has no demonstrable effects on man except for the many untoward effects that come from toxic levels (Nielsen and Ollerich, 1974).

It is obvious that there is a great deal yet to be learned about the role of essential trace elements in the ecology of human health and disease. And knowing which essential trace element does what in a biological system is only a part of the total picture. We need to know much more about the geochemistry of these elements if we are to understand how much of each of them, in what chemical form, reaches the biological system under consideration.

"Nature has never divided herself into the sharply defined areas of chemistry, biochemistry, physics, etc., but rather she has used all the advantages of each branch to design a unique, superbly produced, product" (Williams, 1971). Scientists should not be divided either. They often are, however, as a result of an isolation that comes from concern with only the disciplinary area of their primary interest. All the advantages of each discipline are necessary to understand the complex interactions that reflect health or disease. These advantages can only be realized by a multidisciplinary effort that, in the context of this discussion, involves geologists and geochemists, just as it involves nutritionists and other biomedical scientists.

REFERENCES CITED

Anonymous, 1972, Fluoride and osteoporosis: British Med. Jour., December 30, 1972, 748 p.

Brooks, R. R., 1972, Geobotany and biogeochemistry in mineral exploration: New York, Harper and Row, 290 p.

Cannon, H. L., and Hopps, H. C., 1971,* eds., Environmental geochemistry in human health and disease: Geol. Soc. America Mem. 123, 210 p.

——1972,* eds., Geochemical environment in relation to health and disease: Geol. Soc. America Spec. Paper 140, 77 p.

Carlisle, E. M., 1974, Silicon as an essential element: Fed. Proc., v. 33, p. 1758–1766.

Davis, G. K., 1972, Competition among mineral elements relating to absorption by animals: New York Acad. Sci. Annals, v. 199, p. 62–69.

Hamilton, E. I., and Minski, M. J., 1972, Abundance of the chemical elements in man's diet and possible relations with environmental factors: Science of the Total Environment, v. 1, p. 375–393.

Hopkins, L. L., Jr., and Mohr, H. E., 1974, Vanadium as an essential nutrient: Fed. Proc., v. 33, p. 1773–1775.

Hopps, H. C., 1971, Geographic pathology and the medical implications of environmental geochemistry, in Cannon, H. L., and Hopps, H. C., eds., Environmental geochemistry in human health and disease: Geol. Soc. America Mem. 123, p. 1–11.

——1972, Ecology of disease in relation to environmental trace elements—Particularly iron: Geol. Soc. America Bull., v. 83, p. 797–804.

Hopps, H. C., and Cannon, H. L., 1972,* eds., Geochemical environment in relation to health and disease: New York Acad. Sci. Annals, v. 199, 352 p.

Hopps, H. C., and Cuffey, R. J., 1969, Cause/effect relationships in disease: Internat. Pathology, v. 10, p. 23–25.

Mertz, W., 1970, Some aspects of nutritional trace element research: Fed. Proc., v. 29, p. 1482–1488.

——1972, Human requirements: Basic and optimal: New York Acad. Sci. Annals, v. 199, p. 191–201.

National Academy of Sciences, 1971, Selenium in nutrition, a report by the Committee on Animal Nutrition: p. 51–53.

——1974a, Chromium, a report of the Committee on Biologic Effects of Atmospheric Pollutants: p. 28–34.

——1974b, Effects of fluorides in animals, a report of the Committee on Animal Nutrition: 70 p.

National Academy of Sciences, 1974c, Vanadium, a report of the Committee on Biologic Effects of Atmospheric Pollutants: p. 63–69.
——1974d, Geochemistry and the environment, Vol. 1, *in* The relation of selected trace elements to health and disease: 113 p.
Nielsen, F. H., and Ollerich, D. A., 1974, Nickel: A new trace element: Fed. Proc., v. 33, p. 1767–1772.
Pories, W. J., Mansour, E. G., and Strain, W. H., 1972, Trace elements that act to inhibit neoplastic growth: New York Acad. Sci. Annals, v. 199, p. 265–273.
Schwarz, K., 1974, Recent dietary trace element research, exemplified by tin, fluorine, and silicon: Fed. Proc., v. 33, p. 1748–1757.
Strain, W. H., Pories, W. J., Mansour, E. G., and Flynn, A., 1975, Therapies for environmental element deficiencies and toxic excesses, *in* Freedman, J., ed., Trace element geochemistry in health and disease: Geol. Soc. American Spec. Paper 155, p. 83–106.
Williams, D. R., 1971, The metals of life: London, Van Nostrand Reinhold Co., 172 p.

*References marked with an asterisk are comprehensive in their coverage.

GENERAL REFERENCES

Dhar, S. K., 1973, ed., Metal ions in biological systems: New York, Plenum Press, 306 p.
Frieden, E., 1972, The chemical elements of life: Sci. American, v. 227, p. 52–60.
Kubota, J., and Allaway, W. H., 1972, Geographic distribution of trace element problems, *in* Micronutrients in agriculture: Madison, Wis., Soil Sci. Soc. America, p. 525–554.
Mills, C. F., 1970, ed., Trace element metabolism in animals: Edinburgh, E & S Livingstone, 550 p.
Schroeder, H. A., 1965, The biological trace elements or peripatetics through the periodic table: Jour. Chronic Disease, v. 18, p. 217–228.
Scott, M. L., 1972, Trace elements in animal nutrition, *in* Micronutrients in agriculture: Madison, Wis., Soil Sci. Soc. America, p. 555–591.
Tracing and Treating Mineral Disorders in Dairy Cattle, 1973, prepared by the Committee on Mineral Nutrition: Wageningen, Centre for Agricultural Publishing and Documentation, 6 p.
Underwood, E. J., 1971, Trace elements in human and animal nutrition (3rd ed.): New York, Academic Press, 543 p.

Paper Presented at the 1972 Annual Meeting of the Geological Society of America in Minneapolis, Minnesota
Manuscript Received by the Society September 17, 1973
Revised Manuscript Received November 11, 1974

Geological Society of America
Special Paper 155
© 1975

Man's Effect on the Geochemistry of Lake and Stream Sediments from Southern Ontario

JOHN A. C. FORTESCUE

AND

J. TERASMAE
Department of Geological Sciences
Brock University
St. Catharines, Ontario
Canada, L2S 3A1

ABSTRACT

Preliminary surveys based on lake and stream sediments have been carried out in southern Ontario as a possible basis for geoepidemiological research. The survey of cores of lake sediments involved 40 cores taken from 20 lakes in southern Ontario. Each core was examined for copper, lead, zinc, cadmium, and nickel soluble in acid as well as for fossil pollen that was used to date the sample material. There was a direct relationship between the age of the core material, the location from which the cores were collected, and the trace-element content of the samples. The stream-sediment survey involved the collection of 1,105 samples of material from a 1,165 km² area around St. Catharines, Ontario. In this study, eight elements were determined in the samples, and it was concluded that variations in the distribution patterns for lead, strontium, and zinc were caused by man's activities in some cases and by natural causes in others. It is concluded that surveys of lake or stream sediments may be important starting points for the collection of geochemical data.

INTRODUCTION

It is known that some diseases in plants, animals, or man may result from variations in the distribution, amount, and chemical form of one or more trace elements in the environment in which these organisms live (Treshow, 1970; Underwood, 1971; Hemphill, 1971, 1972; Hopps and Cannon, 1972). The discovery and description of imbalances in the chemistry of the environment is at an early stage of development; and there is a need for fresh approaches to the solution of problems of this type.

Banta and Johnson (1972) discussed considerations in relation to the collection of geochemical information for the solution of epidemiological problems. They stressed that the "what, when, and where" of disease are of paramount importance to the epidemiologist, and geochemical information concerning distribution patterns of particular elements in the environment must also take these considerations into account. We shall stress the importance of the interaction of the hierarchies of space, time, complexity, and effort in the planning of research at the interface between geology and disease.

Although much progress has been made by geochemists in the systematization of the collection of data of interest to epidemiologists, geochemists do not discuss the chemistry of components of landscapes from a holistic viewpoint. For example, in the series of papers included in Hopps and Cannon (1972), the geochemistry of rocks, soil, waters, and plants is treated without reference to a conceptual framework of landscape, such as that described by Glazovskaya (1963). Geochemists, who interact with epidemiologists, must be prepared to try new approaches to the collection of data, which may involve disciplines not usually associated with each other, such as geochemistry and palynology. Such approaches, which involve large areas of country, must be simplified so that the cost of the collection of the data is not prohibitive.

SURVEY PLANNING

The object of the two surveys described here was to establish the feasibility of using lake-sediment cores or stream sediments as a basis for the collection of information. Unfortunately, it was not possible to test these approaches in areas where epidemiological problems are known, although the experience gained will make it a simple matter to carry out similar surveys.

Hierarchy of Space

The extent of the survey of lake sediments was determined by two factors, one extensive and the other intensive. To provide information from a large area of southern Ontario, lakes located in six areas (selected on the basis of geology, land use, history and settlement pattern, climate, and vegetation type) were studied. Within each area, small lakes were selected for core sampling; one or more cores were taken from each lake, depending on conditions (Fig. 1).

The survey of stream sediment was based on techniques and principles that have been proven reliable in Canada for geochemical prospecting (Hawkes and Webb, 1962; Boyle, 1971). For the purpose of this survey, samples were collected from wet (or dry) stream channels located upstream from all road bridges that occur in a 1,165 km^2 area in the vicinity of St. Catharines. Using this technique, a uniform coverage of sample sites was obtained over the area, except where there are no streams (Fig. 1). One area without streams is in the vicinity of

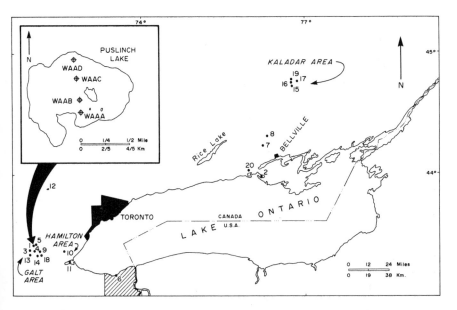

Figure 1. Index map showing location of lakes sampled and area covered by stream-sediment survey (diagonal lines) in southern Ontario, and location of sites of lake-sediment cores in Puslinch Lake.

Fonthill in the south-central part of the surveyed area (Fig. 1). Stream sediments were collected from 1,105 points in the area.

Hierarchy of Time

Since modern man settled southern Ontario in the last 250 years, sediment has accumulated at a variable rate in the lakes of the area. The change in plant cover type (that is, from forest to agriculture) is accompanied by an increase in grass and weed pollen in the air that settles to the bottom of lakes, which indicates when settlement took place. Bassett and Terasmae (1962) and others found that a sharp rise in the abundance of ragweed (*Ambrosia* sp.) pollen in lake sediments is an effective time marker. *Ambrosia* pollen was used to date the sediments in this study (Terasmae and others, 1972). The importance of this approach is that it provides descriptions and dates on changes in the trace-element content of the environment related to man's activities. The need for information of this type has been stressed by epidemiologists (Berg and Burbank, 1972).

The objective of the survey of stream sediments was to obtain a "still picture" of the distribution and amount of eight trace elements in the area. A three-month period was required (during the summer of 1970) to collect the samples. Subsequent research by Gawron (1973) has shown that changes in the content of trace elements soluble in cold hydrochloric acid in samples of stream sediment collected each week over a three-month period are insignificant. The trace-element content of samples collected during the same period from an industrial canal varied considerably, probably because of effluent from industrial plants.

Hierarchy of Complexity

The chemistry of lake sediments is complicated and varied. From the viewpoint of epidemiology, a simple chemical test that would provide information on the distribution and amount of trace elements in cores of lake sediment was needed. These would provide data on significant changes in the chemistry of the environment during ecological time. Of lesser interest is the content of trace elements in primary minerals, which do not contribute directly to the chemistry of the environment. Preliminary experiments using several extractants, applied to a typical set of samples, indicated that the vertical distribution patterns for trace elements in cores of lake sediment and distribution of trace elements in stream sediments were similar. The amount extracted varied with extractant and element extracted. Consequently, a leach of cold hydrochloric acid was chosen for the extraction of trace elements from both sample types. Pretreatment of the lake sediments included drying at 110° C in an oven and dry ashing in a temperature-controlled muffle furnace below 435° C prior to the acid leaching. Pretreatment of the stream sediments included drying at 110° C for 8 hr, crushing the dry material in a mortar, and passing the samples through an 80-mesh sieve. A weighed portion of the −80-mesh material was leached with 12 percent by volume hydrochloric acid for 8 hr in a reciprocating shaker. The reliability of these techniques has been described elsewhere (Gawron, 1973; Fortescue and others, 1972). All element determinations in the extracts were made using a Perkin-Elmer 403 Atomic Absorption spectrophotometer equipped with a teletype printer and an automatic sample changer.

Copper, lead, zinc, cadmium, and nickel soluble in cold hydrochloric acid were determined in the lake-sediment core samples, and the content of these and manganese, iron, and strontium was determined in the stream sediments. Reference will be made to the distribution of only the five elements in lake-sediment cores and to lead, strontium, and zinc in the stream sediments. Details of the distribution patterns for the other elements in the stream sediments have been described (Fortescue and others, 1971; Fortescue, 1972).

Hierarchy of Effort

The geochemist involved in the development of survey methods for the distribution of chemical elements within a particular component of landscape (for example, soils, lakes) must select the most effective technique. The relative effectiveness of survey techniques may be increased by collecting data according to a preconceived, statistically based sampling plan, which is designed to satisfy a set of rules. Another way is to select a component (or components) of landscape for intensive study. A set of detailed geochemical data can be collected from one place and can be compared with similar sets obtained elsewhere. Because of the preliminary nature of our research in relation to conditions in southern Ontario, the second alternative was chosen for this study. A statistical analysis of data from our stream sediments for elements not described here has already been attempted (Black and others, 1971; Fortescue, 1973).

TABLE 1. DATA ON EXTRACTION TECHNIQUE WITH
COLD HYDROCHLORIC ACID APPLIED TO 48 REPLICATES OF A
REFERENCE STANDARD MIXTURE OF ASHED CORES OF LAKE SEDIMENT
INCLUDED IN A BATCH OF 20 UNKNOWN SAMPLES

Element	Mean value (ppm)	Coefficient of variation (%)
Zinc	4.3	10.7
Nickel	1.2	10.9
Lead	2.0	11.1
Cadmium	0.1	12.5
Copper	0.5	14.0

METHODS

Cores of Lake Sediment

Full details of the techniques used to obtain pollen data and for the chemical analysis of lake-sediment cores have been given elsewhere (Fortescue, 1972; Terasmae and others, 1972). In each lake, one or more cores of bottom sediment (to a maximum of 2 m in length) were collected with a Brown sampler (Mott, 1966). The cores of sediment were collected in acrylic resin tubes, which (if possible) were allowed to freeze prior to transport to the laboratory. The cores, cut into 5-cm lengths, were divided into two parts: one represented 1 cm of core length (for pollen analysis), and the other was used for chemical analysis. A total of 1,200 subsamples of lake sediments taken from 40 cores were treated in this way.

The extraction procedure for trace elements in the ashed cores of lake sediments included a reference standard (mixed from excess material obtained from 40 of the unknown cores) with each of the 48 batches of 20 unknown samples (Table 1). The performance of the analytical method (Table 1) was more than adequate for use in the interpretation of the data in the cores of lake sediments.

Samples of Stream Sediment

Details of the collection and techniques of chemical analysis of the samples of stream sediments were described in Fortescue and others (1971). The samples were collected with a clean trowel and placed in waterproof bags. Sample sites were located in the center of wet or dry stream beds, upstream from highway bridges. Two samples were collected from each site, one was used for chemical processing and the other was air dried for comparative analysis when the area was resampled.

The coefficient of variation obtained from repeat analyses of stream-sediment reference standards for lead, strontium, and zinc was of similar magnitude to that obtained for the cores of lake sediment (Fig. 1).

RESULTS

Cores of Lake Sediment

The data in Figure 2 were selected to provide a typical example of the results obtained from a suite of cores of lake sediments taken from a single lake (Puslinch

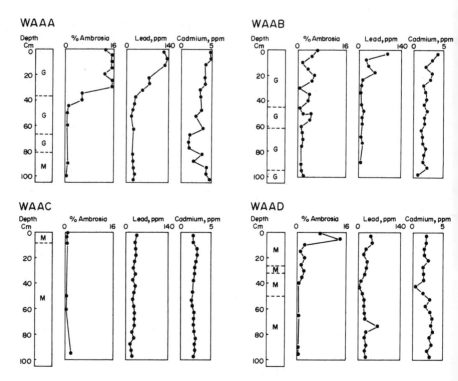

Figure 2. Vertical distribution of *Ambrosia* pollen, lead, and cadmium in each of four sediment cores collected from Puslinch Lake. M = marl; G = gyttja.

Lake, Fig. 1). In each sample, the cores were 1 m long and were composed of gyttja or marl (Fig. 2). The distribution of the *Ambrosia* pollen in the four cores illustrates advantages and disadvantages of this technique. In core WAAA, the *Ambrosia* pollen increases tenfold to a depth of 0.35 cm in the core, whereas in core WAAB, the increase is less marked and at a shallower depth. In core WAAC, the distribution of pollen is relatively uniform and does not include an "*Ambrosia* rise." It is concluded from this example and from others (Terasmae and others, 1972) that the choice of a sample point on a lake bottom may govern the success of the use of pollen to determine the rate of deposition of lake sediments. It is evident from Figure 2 that failure to locate the *Ambrosia* rise in a single core from a lake does not rule out the possibility of finding another area on the bottom of the same lake where measurements can be made.

Data for the vertical distribution of cadmium and lead in the cores from Puslinch Lake (Fig. 2) were different. Little variation was found in the vertical distribution of cadmium, which could be related to the *Ambrosia* rise, although in the lower layers of some cores (for example, WAAA), some fluctuations in the content of this element were observed. The distribution pattern for lead was similar to that for the *Ambrosia* pollen in all four cores. This trend is best observed in core WAAA, where the *Ambrosia* pollen increased, and in core WAAC, where there was no increase in the ragweed pollen count. The experience at Puslinch Lake and elsewhere (Terasmae and others, 1972) indicates that the increase in *Ambrosia* pollen is accompanied by an increase in the lead soluble in acid in the lake sediments.

The nine lakes and the cores were selected from three areas in southern Ontario (Fig. 1). Within each area, information for the content of cadmium, lead, zinc, copper, and nickel above and below the *Ambrosia* rise are shown (Table 2). In all cases, except one, the cores were over 1 m long; they were selected to include cores with *Ambrosia* rise close to and remote from the bottom of the lake. Two of the areas from which the cores were taken (Galt and Hamilton, Table 2) were underlain by Paleozoic limestone and dolostone and one (Kaladar, Table 2) by Precambrian siliceous rocks. Data for the percent ash in the oven-dried material indicates the homogeneity of the cores. A similar average ash content above and below the *Ambrosia* rise was found in the Bishop Lake core and in Lake Medad core "a," whereas in the Hill Lake core and the Lake Medad core "d," the difference was more pronounced.

Ratios for the content of cadmium, zinc, copper, and nickel in the cores before and after the *Ambrosia* rise also appear in Table 2. The content of the trace elements in sediments deposited since man settled the areas is greater than before, although these increases are usually less than threefold, regardless of the depth to the *Ambrosia* rise. It was unusual that the increase in heavy metals was not greater in magnitude in the cores collected from Lake Medad, which is situated near the city of Hamilton, Ontario. One explanation for this low anomaly may be that our extractant (cold acid) is not the best to detect heavy metal pollution, or that drying the sediment may have reduced the amount of trace elements that are extractable. Further research is needed to examine the validity of these possibilities.

The increase in the content of lead in the eight cores of lake sediments taken from basins situated on Paleozoic rocks ranged from 1.9 to 10 times (Table 2). Where the ratio was below 3, it tended to be higher than that found for the other trace elements in the same core. In the four cores collected in the Kaladar area on Precambrian siliceous rocks, the increase in lead was between 13 and 27 times. This is due to the low solubility of lead in cold acid in the pre-*Ambrosia* rise sediment and to the high amount of lead leached from the acid soils in the drainage basin since.

In summary, under favorable conditions, a combination of palynological and geochemical evidence obtained from cores of lake sediments can be used to describe effects of man's activities on the chemistry of the environment of parts of southern Ontario, and the element lead appears to be the heavy metal of greatest interest.

Surveys of Stream Sediment

Geochemical maps showing the distribution of lead (Fig. 3), strontium (Fig. 4), and zinc (Fig. 5) illustrate the type of information that could be used for epidemiological research. We shall consider those areas on the maps where the content of an element in the samples was over four times the mode value calculated for the whole area.

The distribution of lead in the stream sediments of the St. Catharines area is shown in Figure 3. Two types of patterns directly related to man's activities occur on the map. High values for lead at area A are directly related to the proximity of urban St. Catharines or to industrial activity in a rural setting (areas B and C). The high lead in area D is related to the effect of lead compounds in sprays that have been applied to orchards in the area. High values for lead, which were found elsewhere on the map, may be due to man's activities or to natural causes, and more detailed investigations are needed to interpret this aspect of the lead distribution. The advantage of a map of this type for epidemiologists is that it can be used as a transparent overlay on maps showing the distribution of disease in the area and can be interpreted directly. The map of lead values may be used as a starting point for statistical evaluation of the data along the lines described by Black and others (1971).

The distribution of strontium in the stream sediments (Fig. 4) is different from that for lead. There are three clusters of high values, two of which (areas E and F) are in rural areas outside the limits of urban or industrial activity. For this reason, the strontium patterns are probably due to natural causes, and their presence could neither be predicted nor explained on the basis of man's activities. It is patterns of this type, which often cannot be predicted on the basis of geology or man's activities and which can be located by stream-sediment surveys with little effort, that may be of interest to epidemiologists.

Another type of distribution pattern for zinc is found on Figure 5. The high and low values are distributed more or less uniformly across the map, and clustering is not so marked as with the other two elements. There are two areas in Figure 5 where no high values were found; one, H, coincides with area C on Figure 3 and the other, J, coincides with area F in Figure 4. These relationships focus attention on another aspect of the interpretation of geochemical maps based on stream sediments. It concerns the similarity of distribution patterns for elements that may or may not be expected to behave in the same way on the basis of theoretical considerations. Synergistic effects of this type may also be important in geoepidemiology.

In summary, the distribution patterns for lead, strontium, and zinc on regional geochemical maps of a 1,165 km^2 area centered on St. Catharines, Ontario, indicates that there are clusters of high values for each of the elements. Some of the high values can be directly related to man's effect on the chemistry of the environment. Examination of maps for a number of elements may provide clues that could relate the distribution of trace elements in the environment to epidemiological distribution patterns.

DISCUSSION

Two kinds of regional geochemical surveys that might be of value in relation to epidemiological studies have been described for parts of southern Ontario. Data from surveys of lake sediment indicate that variations in the chemistry of the environment associated with man's activities can be dated by evidence from palynology and can be described by means of geochemistry. A similar conclusion was reached by Bortleson and Lee (1972), who studied the *Ambrosia* pollen

TABLE 2. SUMMARY OF PALYNOLOGICAL AND GEOCHEMICAL DATA FROM CORES OF SEDIMENTS FROM NINE LAKES IN SOUTHERN ONTARIO

Area	Lake*	Total core depth (cm)	Depth to Ambrosia rise† (cm)	Percent ash	Cadmium	Zinc	Copper	Nickel	Lead
						Trace-element content (ppm)§			
Kaladar (Fig. 1)	Bishop(15) (CAB)#	130	10	A 55(2)	1.7	160(1.9)	27(0.9)	9(0.8)	75(13)
				B 55(24)**	0.8(2.1)††	83(1.9)	31(0.9)	11(0.8)	6(13)
	Story (16) (CBB)	128	20	A 35(4)	2.4(3.0)	233(5.0)	14(0.6)	15(1.0)	106(27)
				B 28(21)	0.8(3.0)	47(5.0)	24(0.6)	15(1.0)	4(27)
	Cloyne(19) (CCB)	110	30	A 49(6)	1.2(2.0)	108(2.2)	36(0.7)	11	68(23)
				B 52(16)	0.6(2.0)	49(2.2)	54(0.7)	9(1.2)	3(23)
	Hill (17) (CDA)	130	40	A 24(8)	1.5(3.8)	161(2.8)	17(1.4)	13(1.4)	57(14)
				B 15(19)	0.4(3.8)	57(2.8)	12(1.4)	9(1.4)	4(14)
Galt	Puslinch(1) (AAD)	138	10	A 83(2)	2.2(0.9)	92(2.2)	5(1.0)	13(1.2)	44(1.9)
				B 72(25)	2.4(0.9)	41(2.2)	5(1.0)	11(1.2)	23(1.9)
	Moore Pond (18,AFA)	153	20	A 41(4)	1.9(2.4)	139(2.7)	17(2.4)	6(1.7)	81(10)
				B 26(26)	0.8(2.4)	52(2.7)	7(2.4)	6(1.7)	8(10)
	Wrigley(4) (ACA)	45	30	A 57(6)	1.0(1.4)	142(1.0)	6(1.0)	10(1.0)	32(2.1)
				B 59(3)	0.7(1.4)	149(1.0)	6(1.0)	10(1.0)	15(2.1)
	Pinehurst (14,AEA)	130	80	A 50(16)	1.8(2.6)	142(2.0)	10(1.1)	12(1.3)	73(2.3)
				B 34(9)	0.7(2.6)	71(2.0)	9(1.1)	9(1.3)	32(2.3)
Hamilton	Medad-a (10,BAA)	140	15	A 82(3)	2.8(0.9)	158(2.9)	14(1.6)	19(1.1)	61(2.3)
				B 87(25)	3.2(0.9)	55(2.9)	9(1.6)	17(1.1)	27(2.3)
	Medad-b (10,BAB)	141	15	A 81(3)	2.5(1.0)	119(1.6)	12(1.0)	17	43(1.9)
				B 73(24)	2.5(1.0)	73(1.6)	12(1.0)	18(0.9)	23(1.9)
	Medad-c (10,BAC)	148	30	A 75(6)	2.1	211(3.0)	17	18	64
				B 73(23)	2.6(0.8)	70(3.0)	12(1.4)	16(1.1)	26(2.5)
	Medad-d (10,BAD)	135	60	A 70(12)	1.7	223(2.0)	15(0.6)	19(1.9)	51
				B 15(15)	1.0(1.7)	122(2.0)	25(0.6)	10(1.9)	6(9.0)

*Location number on Figure 1.

† Depth of core from present lake bottom to Ambrosia sp. pollen rise.

§ Oven-dried weight.

Identification code for sediment core. For more information, see Terasmae and others (1972).

** Number of subsamples in average estimate.

†† Ratio average content of element in samples located above and below Ambrosia sp. rise.

Figure 3. Lead content soluble in cold hydrochloric acid of the −80-mesh fraction of stream-sediment samples collected from St. Catharines area expressed as parts per million oven-dry weight. Dots = content of sample was four times mode value. Circles = other sample sites. Numbers do not relate to magnitude of geochemical data.

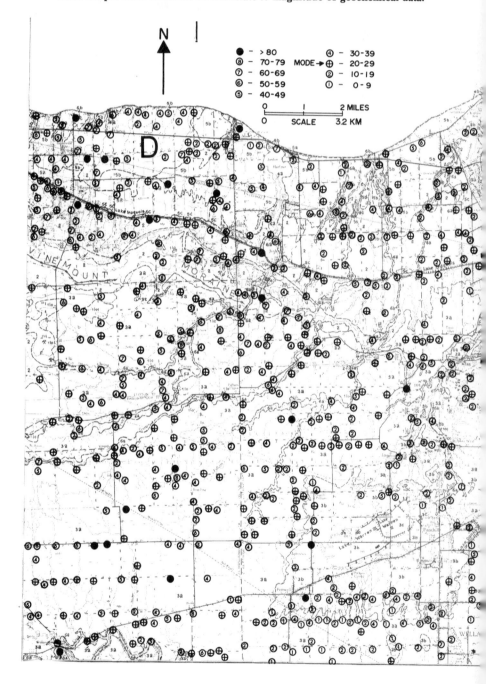

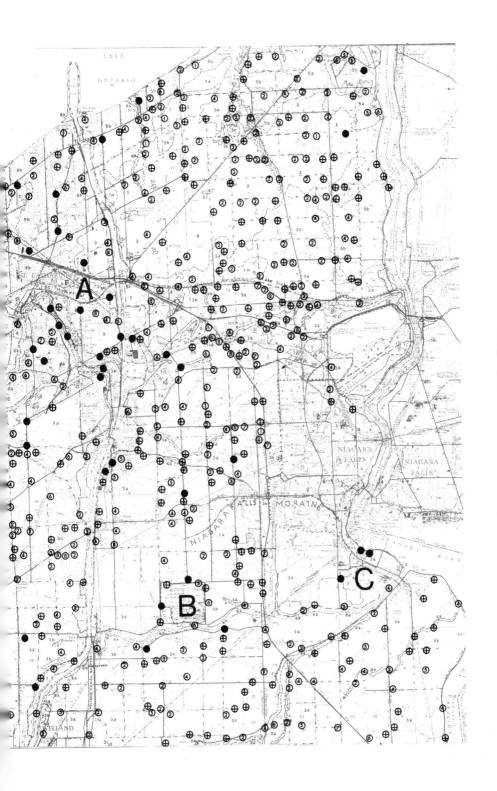

Figure 4. Strontium content soluble in cold hydrochloric acid of the −80-mesh fraction of stream-sediment samples collected from St. Catharines area expressed as parts per million oven-dry weight.

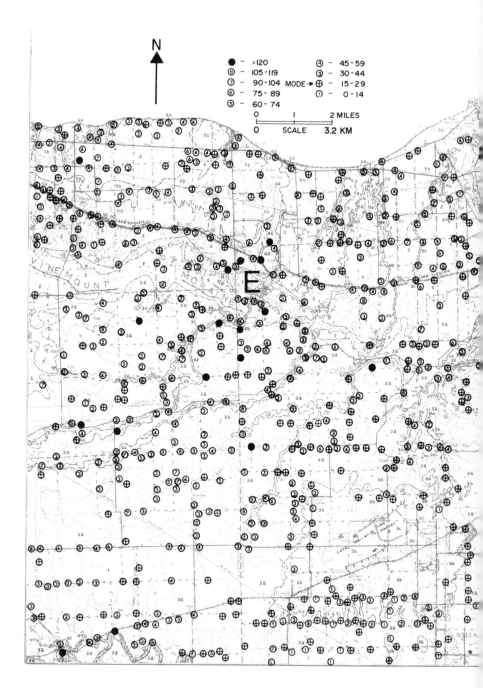

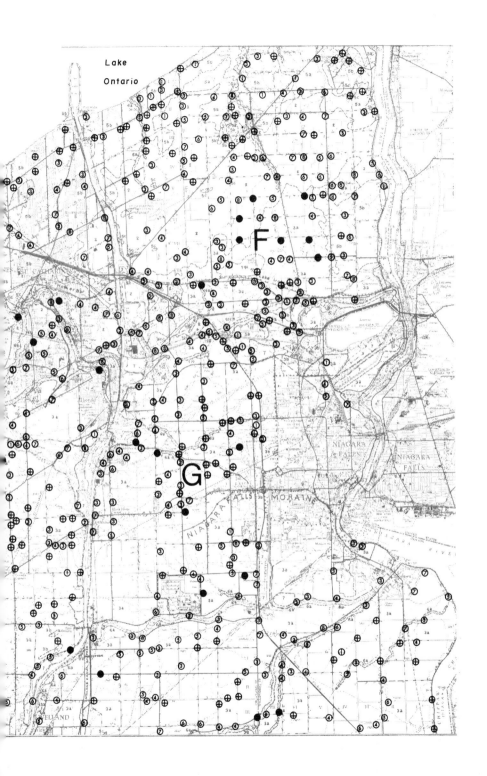

Figure 5. Zinc content soluble in cold hydrochloric acid of the −80-mesh fraction of stream-sediment samples collected from St. Catharines area expressed as parts per million oven dry weight.

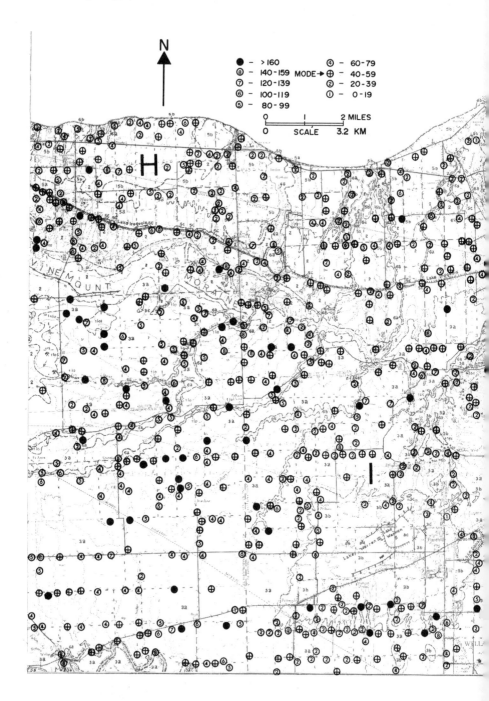

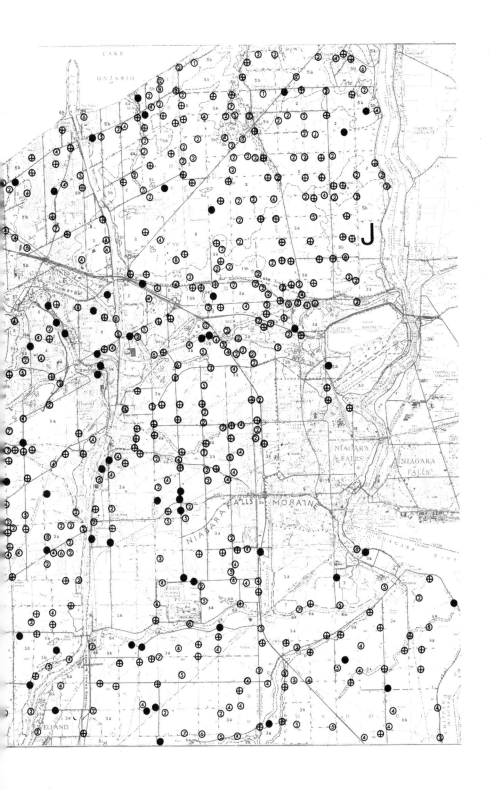

distribution and the geochemistry of lake sediments obtained from Lake Mendota, Wisconsin. They found that a long period of stable watershed conditions existed prior to the settlement period in Wisconsin.

The use of stream sediments to detect man's effect on the geochemistry of the environment in the vicinity of St. Catharines, Ontario, has been outlined for the elements lead, strontium, and zinc. Some of the distribution patterns were related to man's activities and others to natural causes. Relationships between stream-sediment geochemistry and disease in animals (or man) have been described. For example, Thornton and Webb (1970) discussed the use of stream sediments to demonstrate relationships between suspected pine in sheep and cattle and the cobalt content of the environment. They also used stream sediments to outline areas of high molybdenum and selenium content in an area where low levels of blood copper were found in grazing cattle.

The approach to surveys of lake sediment and stream sediment described here was designed with simplicity in mind. Consequently, our choice of sample collection, sample processing, and chemical-analysis techniques was dictated by previous experience involving the collection of large amounts of data. It may be argued that our surveys should have been more intensive and, for example, should have involved the wet processing of sediment samples using different extracting agents for particular heavy metals. We think that our approach was an effective means for collection of preliminary data with little effort. Consequently, we believe that the techniques described here provide epidemiologists with considerable information with a minimum of effort. As the study of geoepidemiology becomes more sophisticated, problems of sample collection and processing will be solved and the ability to determine large numbers of chemical elements in materials of this type on a routine basis will be established.

This discussion leads us directly to the problem of standardization of the planning of geochemical and epidemiological studies undertaken in the same area. Close attention to the hierarchies of space, time, complexity, and effort will be needed as a basis for standardization of this type. Only when a holistic approach is adopted at the planning stage of the project will the most effective methods of data collection be discovered.

CONCLUSIONS

1. Under favorable conditions, cores of lake sediments could be used to describe changes that had occurred during the recent past in the geochemistry of the environment of southern Ontario.

2. On the basis of studies of the distribution of the *Ambrosia* pollen in the cores of lake sediments, it was possible to relate these changes to man's settlement of the area.

3. Of the five heavy metals studied in the cores of lake sediment (that is, cadmium, zinc, copper, nickel, and lead), only lead was found to vary consistently with the distribution of *Ambrosia* pollen at Puslinch Lake (Fig. 2).

4. Some of the distribution patterns for lead, strontium, and zinc in stream sediments from the St. Catharines area could be directly attributed to man's activities.

5. In the strontium distribution map (Fig. 4), areas of high values could not

be related directly to geological or land-use data. It is concluded that patterns of this type are of particular interest to epidemiologists.

6. It is concluded that in spite of the crude approach, which was deliberately adopted for both types of surveys (to make them as extensive as possible with the resources available), information was obtained that is of direct interest to epidemiologists.

7. It was concluded that geochemists and epidemiologists should cooperate at the planning stage of geochemical surveys based on lake sediments or stream sediments so that a holistic approach may be taken to the design of geoepidemiological surveys.

REFERENCES CITED

Banta, J. A., and Johnson, J., 1972, Disease data: Epidemiological considerations: New York Acad. Sci. Annals, v. 199, p. 294–300.

Bassett, I. J., and Terasmae, J., 1962, Ragweeds, *Ambrosia* species, in Canada and their history in post-glacial time: Canadian Jour. Botany 40, p. 141–150.

Berg, J. W., and Burbank, F., 1972, Correlations between carcinogenic trace metals in water supplies and cancer mortality: New York Acad. Sci. Annals, v. 199, p. 249–265.

Black, J. E., Westera, K., and Fortescue, J.A.C., 1971, The use of elliptical areas for a preliminary statistical interpretation of reconnaissance stream sediment maps of the St. Catharines area, Ontario: St. Catharines, Ontario, Brock Univ., Dept. Geol. Sci. Research Rept., no. 4, p. 29.

Bortleson, G. C., and Lee, G. F., 1972, Recent sedimentary history of Lake Mendota, Wis.: Environmental Sci. and Technology, v. 6, no. 9, p. 799–808.

Boyle, R. W., ed., 1971, Geochemical exploration: Canadian Inst. Mining and Metallurgy (CIM), Spec. Vol. 11, p. 594.

Fortescue, J.A.C., 1972, A preliminary study of relationships between patterns on topographic, geological, land use and geochemical maps of the area around St. Catharines, Ontario, *in* Hemphill, D. D., ed., Trace substances in environmental health, Proc., V: Columbia, Univ. Missouri Press, p. 497–514.

——1973, The need for conceptual thinking in geoepidemiological research, *in* Hemphill, D. D., ed., Trace substances in environmental health, Proc., VI: Columbia, Univ. Missouri Press, p. 333–339.

Fortescue, J.A.C., Dupuis, J., Hughes, J., Winn, R., Gawron, E., and Ernesaks, I., 1971, A preliminary study of the use of stream sediment geochemistry to detect the effects of man's activities on the environment around St. Catharines, Ontario: St. Catharines, Ontario, Brock Univ., Dept. Geol. Sci.

Fortescue, J.A.C., Curtis, S. A., and Gawron, E., 1972, A semiautomated laboratory for teaching and research in landscape geochemistry: Canada Jour. Spectroscopy, v. 18, no. 1, p. 23–29.

Gawron, E., 1973, The effect of collecting time and grain size on sampling stream sediments for geochemical mapping in the St. Catharines area: St. Catharines, Ontario, Brock Univ., Dept. Geol. Sci. Research Rept., no. 3, p. 65.

Glazovskaya, M. A., 1963, On geochemical principles of the classification of natural landscapes: Internat. Geol. Rev., v. 5, no. 11, p. 1403–1431.

Hawkes, H. E., and Webb, J. S., 1962, Geochemistry in mineral exploration: New York, Harper and Row, 414 p.

Hemphill, D. D., ed., 1971, Trace substances in environmental health, IV: Columbia, Univ. Missouri Press, p. 456.

Hemphill, D. D., ed., 1972, Trace substances in environmental health, IV: Columbia, Univ Missouri Press, p. 559.

Hopps, H. C., and Cannon, H. L., 1972, Geochemical environment in relation to health and disease: New York Acad. Sci. Annals, v. 199, p. 352.

Mott, R. J., 1966, Quaternary palynological sampling techniques of the Geological Survey of Canada: Geol. Survey Canada Paper 66–41, p. 24.

Terasmae, J., Fortescue, J.A.C., Flint, J. J., Gawron, E. F., Winn, R. F., and Winn, C E., 1972, Palynology and chemistry of lake sediment cores from southern Ontario related to man's activities on the environment: St. Catharines, Ontario, Brock Univ. Dept. Geol. Sci. Research Rept., no. 10, p. 160.

Thornton, I., and Webb, J. S., 1970, Geochemical reconnaissance and the detection o trace element disorders in animals, in Mills, C. F., ed., Trace element metabolism in animals: Edinburgh, Livingstone Press, p. 397–410.

Treshow, M., 1970, Environment and plant response: New York, McGraw Hill, p. 422.

Underwood, E. J., 1971, Trace elements in human and animal nutrition (3rd ed.): New York, Academic Press, p. 543.

PAPER PRESENTED AT THE 1972 ANNUAL MEETING OF THE GEOLOGICAL SOCIETY OF AMERICA IN MINNEAPOLIS, MINNESOTA

MANUSCRIPT RECEIVED BY THE SOCIETY JANUARY 24, 1974

REVISED MANUSCRIPT RECEIVED NOVEMBER 7, 1974

Geological Society of America
Special Paper 155
© 1975

Some Possible Relationships of Water and Soil Chemistry to Cardiovascular Diseases in Indiana

RONALD W. KLUSMAN
Department of Chemistry-Geochemistry
Colorado School of Mines
Golden, Colorado 80401

AND

HERBERT I. SAUER
Environmental Health Surveillance Center
University of Missouri
Columbia, Missouri 65201

ABSTRACT

Recent studies have presented the relationship of various geological, ground-water chemistry, and other environmental factors to death rates for cardiovascular-renal (CVR) and other chronic diseases in the same geographic areas. Several studies report a negative correlation of hardness in the drinking water with CVR diseases death rates. Other studies do not support the hypothesis of a protective role for hard water. In view of the complexity of the environment, other variables in the physical environment, as well as cultural and socioeconomic factors, also require careful consideration.

In Indiana, a variation in CVR diseases death rates follows the Wisconsinan glacial boundary and areas of Wisconsinan outwash, with higher rates north of the boundary. Between these areas, there is a significant difference in soil pH, soil organic carbon, hardness, and possible sulfate in municipal water supplies. For the 92 counties of Indiana, CVR death rates for white males, ages 35 to 74 (age-adjusted), for 1959–1961 show a significant correlation with soil parameters pH and organic carbon, hardness of the drinking water, population density, occupation, income, dust in the air, and other variables. Multiple correlation of eight variables with CVR diseases death rates produces a value of 0.49. Additional measures of the death rate for varying time periods confirm the general conclusions.

Although this moderately homogeneous group of counties presents problems in analysis, the study suggests that many variables often not taken into account may exert considerable influence. An appreciation of the complexity of environmental factors is needed in order to proceed with appropriate caution in the study of the extent and nature of the relationship of geological variables to chronic diseases rates.

INTRODUCTION

Recent studies have shown a geographic variation in death rates for CVR and other chronic diseases. In a search for reasons for such differences, many environmental factors have been shown to have a statistical relationship to the death rate. Several of these environmental variables are influenced or controlled by geological processes.

Sauer and Enterline (1959) noted differences in CVR death rates between states. For the broad category of cardiovascular diseases, evidence is presented from studies by others, as well as from analyses of the data, that differences in rates are not due to methods of collecting or classifying data, and therefore appear to be real. (For narrowly defined cause categories, this general conclusion may not always be valid.) Nor are low rates associated with high indices of medical care.

Schroeder (1960, 1966) showed a negative correlation of CVR diseases death rates with water hardness for the largest cities of the United States. Morris and others (1961) and Crawford and others (1968) showed a similar relation in Great Britain. Studies of this nature led to the hypothesis that the hardness of drinking water exerted some protective role and reduced the risk of cardiovascular death. Lindeman and Assenzo (1964), in a study of Oklahoma CVR diseases death rates, and Buechley and others (1966, unpub. data) presented evidence contrary to the hypothesized protective role of hard water.

Winton and McCabe (1969) and Masironi (1969) summarized the data on drinking-water quality and CVR diseases death rates. Sauer and others (1971) showed a moderate negative correlation of death rates with dissolved solids, hardness, sodium, and potassium in the drinking water of 95 metropolitan areas. They emphasized that other physical and cultural variables may exert considerable influence on death rates. The negative correlation of sodium with death rates may be countered with the laboratory and clinical evidence linking dietary sodium with congestive heart failure and hypertension.

Shacklette and others (1970, 1972) examined the trace-element content of soil and vegetation in relation to CVR death rate in high- and low-rate regions of Georgia. Trace-element content of the soil was different in the two regions, and levels were apparently controlled by parent material, pH, and degree of leaching. A causal relationship to human health in the two regions was not proven but, if present, would be the result of a deficiency of trace elements rather than an excess.

AREA OF STUDY

This study is concerned with the relationship of geology and socioeconomic factors to CVR death rates in Indiana. The 92 counties of Indiana comprise a moderately homogeneous population group, primarily of northern European extraction with only a few counties having nonwhite populations greater than five percent. The death rates utilized in the study include (1) CVR death rates for white males, ages 35 to 74, for the period 1959–1961; (2) natural causes death rates for white males, ages 35 to 74, for the period 1959–1961; (3) all causes death rates for white males, ages 35 to 74, for the period 1959–1969, excluding eight counties that have large resident institutions; and (4) same as 3 above, but for females. The rates are for counties, and rates 1 through 4 are age adjusted by 10-year groups by the direct method to total United States population, ages 35 to 74 in 1950 (Linder and Grove, 1943, p. 66). The rates were calculated from tabulations of deaths by the National Center for Health Statistics, with population-at-risk obtained from Bureau of the Census counts. The most intensive study utilized rate 1, and the other rates served primarily as checks on the general conclusions.

The surficial geology of the state of Indiana is variable because of the influence of glaciation. The entire state is underlain by Paleozoic-age sediments. The state was divided into six geographic divisions based upon the surficial geology and soils (Fig. 1). The northern two-thirds of Indiana is covered by Wisconsinan glacial till of considerable thickness. The drainage is somewhat deranged and poorly developed, particularly in the northeastern part of the state. The southwestern

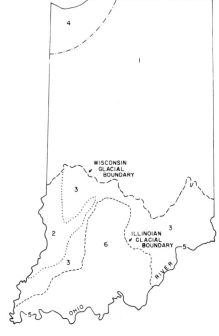

Figure 1. Generalized surficial geology of Indiana. Area 1, Wisconsinan drift; 2, Wisconsinan outwash and loess; 3, Illinoian drift; 4, Wisconsinan dune and beach sands; 5, Ohio River alluvium; 6, unglaciated residual soils.

part was covered by Illinoian glacial till and cut during Wisconsinan time by large glacial sluiceways with deposition of considerable amounts of Wisconsinan outwash and loess. The southeast part is dominated by moderately leached Illinoian glacial till with well-developed drainage. The south-central area was unglaciated and consists of a residual soil covering variable rock types that range from siltstone and sandstone to limestone with well-developed karst.

For the purposes of analysis, the state was divided into only two divisions based on the surficial geology. Regions 1, 2, and 4 (Fig. 1) were grouped together, and regions 3, 5, and 6 were grouped together because of similarities. Because county lines do not follow geologic boundaries, a county was placed according to which region the bulk of the population lived and (or) the location of the county seat.

RELATIONSHIP OF HEALTH AND ENVIRONMENTAL INFLUENCES

Figure 2 shows a histogram of the CVR death rate for the two major regions. Counties in regions 1, 2, and 4 are classed as "counties affected by Wisconsinan glaciation," and regions 3, 5, and 6 are classed as "counties not affected by Wisconsinan glaciation." This notation is used in subsequent figures. The counties affected by Wisconsinan glaciation have a mean CVR death rate of 890.8, standard deviation 98.2; the counties not affected by Wisconsinan glaciation have a mean CVR death rate of 807.7, standard deviation 105.3. A t test for difference in means gave a value of 3.72, for a significant difference at the 0.001 level, which indicates that CVR death rates are significantly higher in the area north of the Wisconsinan glacial boundary or that area underlain by Wisconsinan outwash and loess.

Water

The influence of water quality was considered in relation to the CVR death rate in the two major regions. In the areas of Wisconsinan till and outwash, there is a heavy reliance upon ground water as a municipal water source. In the other areas, surface water supplies assume more importance. Table 1 gives the character of municipal sources for the two major regions. The differences in the sources indicate that a difference in water quality is probable for the two regions. Variable depth of wells reflecting widely differing geologic units

TABLE 1. CHARACTER OF AQUIFER FOR MUNICIPALITIES

	North of Wisconsinan till and outwash boundary		South of Wisconsinan till and outwash boundary	
	Number of municipalities	Percent of total	Number of municipalities	Percent of total
Wells in sand and (or) gravel	274	68.6	78	46.7
Wells in rock	71	17.8	10	6.0
Surface supply	48	12.0	74	44.8
Unknown	6	1.5	4	2.4

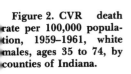

Figure 2. CVR death rate per 100,000 population, 1959–1961, white males, ages 35 to 74, by counties of Indiana.

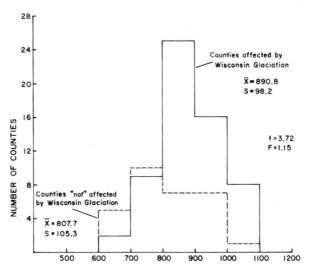

being tapped is not a serious problem. The municipal wells (98) on which depth was available give an average of 214 ft with a maximum of 500 ft. Generally, even the municipal wells are fairly shallow, and the glacial till and alluvium are a good source of water supply. Data for the characterization of water quality are taken from the Indiana State Board of Health (1968) and include at least one analysis for each of the 566 municipalities on public water systems. Where there are multiple sources or multiple analyses, a weighted analysis is calculated. Field analyses of private supplies are not used because of the limited use of a particular source.

The constituents normally analyzed and included in the study (Indiana State Board of Health, 1968) were carbonate hardness (Ca, Mg, Na, K, Fe, Mn); alkalinity; chloride; sulfate; nitrate; and fluoride. Finished water analyses are used where possible as this would better reflect the quality of water that is being consumed by the population. Figure 3 shows the distribution of carbonate hardness for the two major regions, excluding those municipal systems with some degree of softening. Not a large number of people drink softened water, and softening of water in rural areas is minimal. The t test for differences in means for the two major regions is significant at the 0.001 level. Figures 4 and 5 show the distributions of Ca and Mg for the two major regions, respectively. Being components of hardness, Ca and Mg would be expected to show differences. The t test for differences in the means is significant at the 0.01 level for Ca and above the 0.001 level for Mg. In this preliminary analysis, other major constituents, particularly Na, which is frequently implicated as having an influence on health characteristics of a population, did not exhibit differences between the two major regions.

Soil

Another aspect of geochemistry that can be considered in relation to human health is soil composition. Soil and parent material composition exert an influence upon water chemistry, vegetation, and to some extent diets, although they are not composed of strictly locally grown food. Shacklette and others (1970, 1972) considered some of these aspects in a study of high and low death-rate regions of Georgia.

In an examination of soil chemistry of Indiana, the study was restricted to the C horizon that would be closer to equilibrium with ground water and would show the least disturbance by man. The common application of P, K, ammonia, lime, and manure alters the composition and pH of the A and B horizons. Unfortunately, the chemical data are scarcer for the C horizon than for the A and B horizons. Available published (U.S. Department of Agriculture, 1967) and unpublished (Purdue University Soil Survey Laboratory) data that include the C horizon yielded 144 samples of uneven geographic distribution from 31 counties and from five of the six geographic divisions of the state.

Figure 6 is a plot of soil pH data in a histogram form similar to the finished water-quality data. The C horizon in the area covered by Wisconsinan glacial till and Wisconsinan outwash and loess has a significantly higher pH than the area not affected by Wisconsinan glaciation. The soils in the area of Wisconsinan glaciation are much younger, more poorly drained, and have a higher percentage of humus, which grades into muck soils in some areas. The soils of the area to the south of the Wisconsinan glacial boundary are mature, better drained, and more strongly leached. The t value of 8.70 is significant well above the 0.001 level.

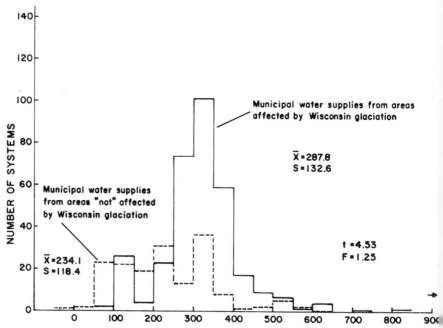

Figure 3. Water hardness as $CaCo_3$ in mg/l. Finished water, excluding those systems with softening.

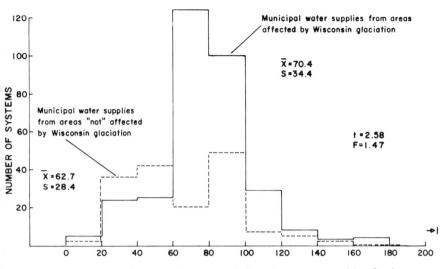

Figure 4. Ca in mg/l. Finished water, excluding those systems with softening.

Figure 7 displays organic carbon, a second soil variable that shows significant differences between the two major regions. Analytical data for organic carbon were available on only 60 samples of the C horizon. The samples from the area affected by Wisconsinan glaciation have a significantly higher mean but also a high standard deviation. This wider range for organic carbon reflects variation in the degree of leaching, depending upon the slope and drainage at the point of sampling. The older soils south of the Wisconsinan glacial boundary show more homogeneity, and local variations in drainage and leaching are averaged out. Other soil parameters were generally not measured for the C horizon, and insufficient data prevent a meaningful analysis.

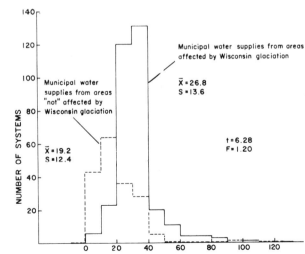

Figure 5. Mg in mg/l. Finished water, excluding those systems with softening.

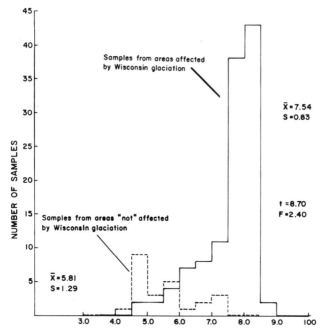

Figure 6. Samples from the C horizon; pH of soils.

Socioeconomic Factors

In a study of this nature, certain socioeconomic and other environmental factors are frequently of importance. One socioeconomic factor to be considered was religion. It was noted that a few counties in the high CVR death rate area north of the Wisconsinan glacial boundary had rather low CVR death rates. In each case, however, the county in question has a high proportion of Amish, Mennonites, or other religious sects of fundamentalist beliefs (National Council of the Churches of Christ in the U.S.A., 1957). The percentage of the county population of fundamentalist belief was estimated for 1960 using the 1957 National Council of Churches data and a linear interpolation of the total county population in 1950 and 1960. The religious beliefs of fundamentalists forbid smoking and drinking, encourage farming practices that require more exercise, and in other ways may possibly lower their CVR death rates. Further, these counties are mainly agricultural. If the twelve counties with the highest percentages of people of fundamentalist belief are excluded, the degree of separation of the two major regions increases. The counties with greater than seven percent of the total population of fundamentalist belief are listed in Table 2. All twelve of these counties are in the area affected by Wisconsinan glaciation and effectively eliminated the lowest CVR death rate counties in this region. The mean CVR death rate for the Wisconsinan glaciated region increased from 890.8 to 901.5, and the standard deviation decreased from 98.2 to 93.0. The t value increased from 3.72 to 4.16, significant well above the 0.001 level (Fig. 8).

Another socioeconomic factor, which frequently has an influence on CVR death

TABLE 2. COUNTIES WITH A HIGH PERCENTAGE FUNDAMENTALISTS

County	Percentage
Adams	8.3
Carroll	8.4
Elkhart	15.7
Grant	7.3
Hamilton	8.7
Henry	9.0
Huntington	8.6
La Grange	12.8
Marshall	7.1
Miami	9.3
Randolph	9.5
Wabash	12.3

rates, is population density. The simplest measure of population density is population per square mile. However, in counties where there is a high proportion of the total population living in a small part of the county, the stress or crowding factor may be higher than simple population per square mile would indicate. Another measure of the stress factor, which might be superior, is the proportion of the county population living in multifamily dwellings and apartments.

A simple correlation of population density versus CVR death rate was moderately significant, approaching the 0.05 level. The distribution of population density was not normal as is frequently the case for sociological variables. The simple parametric correlation may not have been adequate, so a nonparametric Spearman rank correlation was computed. Table 3 suggests that population density or environmental stress, measured in two different ways, has a direct relation to CVR death rates and must be considered in any additional analysis. It seems reasonable to suggest that population density increases cultural stress.

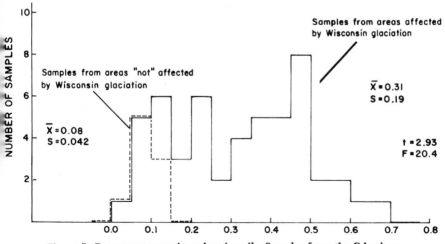

Figure 7. Percentage organic carbon in soils. Samples from the C horizon.

TABLE 3. SPEARMAN RANK CORRELATION OF CVR DEATH RATE AND
POPULATION DENSITY

	Number of counties	Correlation	Significance
Density (population/mi^2)	92	0.313	0.99
Density (% in multifamily dwellings)	92	0.324	>0.99

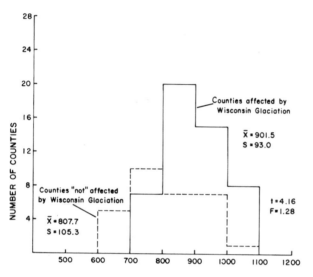

Figure 8. CVR death rate per 100,000 population, 1959–1961, white males, ages 35 to 74, by counties of Indiana, excluding those counties with more than 7 percent fundamentalists.

REGRESSION ANALYSIS AND SPEARMAN RANK CORRELATION OF ENVIRONMENTAL INFLUENCES

The second phase of the study involved incorporating additional factors into the analysis and study by stepwise regression and nonparametric techniques. A single value of each parameter being analyzed was obtained for each county. A mean composition for each constituent being consumed by the population was calculated from the composition of each municipal supply in the county, weighted according to the population served. A composition for the rural population not on a municipal supply was assumed to be the average of all of the raw-water data for that county. The rural population (on private supplies and about which assumptions are made) represents 35 percent ±2 percent of the total population of the state. The uncertainty is due to different census information on the population that is served by the water system for each municipality. In no case was an estimate used, because every county had at least one municipal supply for a basis of water quality.

A similar method, utilizing multiple analyses, might be used to calculate a mean soil composition for each county. This would result, however, in many estimated values instead of measured values for variables that exhibit a moderately high variability over a relatively short distance. Many of the counties have no soil data for the C horizon, and to make an assumption for soil composition would violate the statistical tests.

Air-pollution data were included in the second phase of the study. Quarterly determinations of several air-quality parameters for a 3-yr period for each metropolitan area and three rural sites (Indiana Air Pollution Control Board, 1969, 1970, 1971) were used to determine an average air-quality index for each county. Estimated values for the remaining rural counties were used because the variance in the three rural sites was small. Actual measurements were available for each metropolitan county where considerable variation in air quality is found.

Additional socioeconomic factors include the following: (1) median age for white males, which in the U.S. at present is determined to a very substantial extent by migration patterns, that is, rural counties have lost many young adults through out migration, while urban and suburban counties have gained young adults and their children; (2) percentages of employed workers in white-collar occupations, reflecting level of physical activity and perhaps general health; and (3) median income of families as a possible reflection of quality of health care and general affluence.

The stepwise regression computes a sequence of multiple linear regression equations by adding variables one at a time. The variable added is one that results in the greatest reduction in the error sum of squares or is equivalent to the variable that has the highest partial correlation with the CVR death rate. Variables are deleted when their F values become too low. The stepwise computation continues until the probability of F drops below 0.01.

Table 4 presents the results of the stepwise multiple regression analysis of the CVR death rate for white males, ages 35 to 74, for the period 1959–1961 as dependent variables. The table lists the independent variables in order of significance. The percentage in multifamily dwellings, which is a measure of population density, is considered most important, followed by a group of water- and air-quality variables and socioeconomic factors. The first eight variables result in a multiple correlation coefficient of 0.49. Considering the results of the t test on soil parameters for the two regions, these factors are significant. However, soils variables were not included in this regression because of the uncertainty

TABLE 4. STEPWISE MULTIPLE REGRESSION OF CVR DEATH RATE, 1959–1961, WHITE MALES AGES 35 TO 74*

Variable entered	R	R-squared	F-ratio
Percent in multifamily dwellings	0.303	0.092	9.09
Median age	0.399	0.159	7.12
Ca in water	0.435	0.189	3.25
Sulfation rate of air	0.458	0.210	2.27
K in water	0.465	0.216	0.71
Percent of fundamentalist beliefs	0.472	0.222	0.67
Mg in water	0.481	0.231	0.95
Hardness of water	0.488	0.238	0.74

*BMD 02R, Efroymsen method.

TABLE 5. SPEARMAN RANK CORRELATION OF CVR DEATH RATE, 1959-1961, WHITE MALES AGES 35 TO 74

Variable	R	Significance
Percent in multifamily dwellings	0.324	>0.99
Population density	0.313	>0.99
Percent in white-collar occupations	0.249	>0.99
Dust in air	0.216	>0.95
Median age	0.186	>0.95
Hardness of water	0.156	>0.90
Percent of fundamentalist beliefs	0.147	>0.90
SO_2 in air	0.124	. .
Sulfation rate of air	0.121	. .
NO_2 in air	0.112	. .
Median family income	0.112	. .
Ca in°water	0.109	. .
SO_4 in water	0.098	. .
Mg in water	0.062	. .
Na in water	−0.005	. .

in estimating soil composition for those counties with no soils data.

Most commonly used statistical tests are parametric and cannot be rigorously applied where the data are not normally distributed. Several of the variables included do not have normal distributions so correlations should be checked using a nonparametric test. Table 5 shows the nonparametric Spearman rank correlation of the same variables as Table 4 plus additional variables. Again, soil variables are not included because of the high proportion of counties with no data. Generally, the same variables have high correlations with CVR death rates and serve as a check on the stepwise regression. The additional variable, population density, is another measure of stress, similar to the percentage in multifamily dwellings listed in Table 3, and confirmed by the values of R. The last variable, Na in water, which is frequently recognized as a significant factor in hypertension, has almost a zero correlation.

As a check on the validity of the death rate, other measures of the rate for different time periods were utilized as the dependent variable, and the stepwise regression was recalculated. Table 6 is for natural causes; Table 7 is for all causes, excluding eight counties with large resident institutions. The eight counties are

TABLE 6. STEPWISE MULTIPLE REGRESSION OF NATURAL CAUSES DEATH RATE, 1959-1961, WHITE MALES AGES 35 TO 74*

Variable entered	R	R-squared	F-ratio
Percent in multifamily dwellings	0.335	0.112	11.36
Median age	0.452	0.205	10.34
K in water	0.481	0.231	3.05
Ca in water	0.496	0.246	1.69
Mg in water	0.506	0.256	1.14
Na in water	0.513	0.263	0.86
SO_4 in water	0.528	0.279	1.82
Sulfation rate of air	0.535	0.286	0.90

*BMD 02R, Efroymsen method.

TABLE 7. STEPWISE MULTIPLE REGRESSION OF ALL CAUSES DEATH RATE, 1959–1961, WHITE MALES AGES 35 TO 74*

Variable entered	R	R-squared	F-ratio
Dust in air	0.318	0.101	9.24
Median age	0.441	0.195	9.41
Percent in white-collar occupations	0.498	0.248	5.70
Median family income	0.518	0.269	2.22
Percent in multifamily dwellings	0.529	0.280	1.23
Ca in water	0.534	0.284	0.51
Mg in water	0.548	0.300	1.69
Na in water	0.556	0.310	0.99

*BMD 02R, Efroymsen method.

excluded because adequate data on the resident institution population for this entire time period was not available for adjusting the death rate. Table 8 is for all causes, white females, excluding the eight counties with large resident institutions.

The results of Tables 4, 6, 7, and 8 are generally consistent; the same independent variables are significant, although the order of variables is not the same. Also, the variance explained by the independent variables is similar in each case, which indicates that the different death rates used in the computations are internally consistent, and the observations are not strictly a function of the particular death rate used in the analysis.

SUMMARY

There are undoubtedly other significant variables that would exhibit a strong association with the CVR death rate. Trace elements, for which almost no data were available, might prove significant, particularly in view of the strong differences in soil pH for the two major regions. The control of trace-element solubility, availability to plants, and organic carbon content of soil as a function of pH is marked. Ethnic origin is probably a minor influence in this case because of the northern European ancestry of most of the white population of Indiana and similar health characteristics. The results of this study indicate that the hypothesized

TABLE 8. STEPWISE MULTIPLE REGRESSION OF ALL CAUSES DEATH RATE, 1959–1969, WHITE FEMALES AGES 35 TO 74*

Variable entered	R	R-squared	F-ratio
Percent of fundamentalist belief	0.271	0.073	6.49
Median age	0.338	0.114	3.72
Percent in multifamily dwellings	0.408	0.166	5.04
Mg in water	0.427	0.182	1.49
Ca in water	0.473	0.224	4.16
Na in water	0.482	0.232	0.91
SO_4 in water	0.491	0.242	0.89
Hardness of water	0.495	0.245	0.37

*BMD 02R, Efroymsen method.

protective role of hard water is not confirmed in Indiana; to the extent that there is a correlation, it may be positive.

The relationship of chronic diseases death rates with environmental factors is extremely complex. Most of these diseases are not due to a single simple cause. Geological variables may exert an influence, but caution must be exercised to prevent an oversimplification of the problem and a tendency to equate statistical correlation with a causal effect.

REFERENCES CITED

Crawford, M. D., Gardner, M. J., and Morris, J. N., 1968, Mortality and hardness of local water supplies: Lancet, v. 8, p. 827–831.

Indiana Air Pollution Control Board, 1969, 1968–1969 Annual report: 26 p.

——1970, 1969–1970 Annual report: 12 p.

——1971, 1970–1971 Annual report: 52 p.

Indiana State Board of Health, 1968, Data on Indiana public water supplies: Bull. SE10, 83 p.

Lindeman, R. D., and Assenzo, M. S., 1964, Correlation between water hardness and cardiovascular deaths in Oklahoma counties: Am. Jour. Public Health, v. 54, p. 1071–1077.

Linder, F. E., and Grove, R. D., 1943, Vital statistics rates in the United States, 1900–1940: Washington, D.C., U.S. Govt. Printing Office, 1051 p.

Masironi, R., 1969, Trace elements and cardiovascular diseases: World Health Organization Bull., v. 40, no. 2, p. 305–312.

Morris, J. N., Crawford, M. D., and Heady, J. A., 1961, Hardness of local water supplies and mortality from cardiovascular disease in the county boroughs of England and Wales: Lancet, v. 1, p. 860.

National Council of the Churches of Christ in the U.S.A., 1957, Churches and church membership in the United States—An enumeration and analysis by counties, states and regions: Ser. C, nos. 12, 13, 16 p.

Sauer, H. I., and Enterline, P. E., 1959, Are geographic variations in death rates for the cardiovascular diseases real?: Jour. Chronic Diseases, v. 10, p. 513–524.

Sauer, H. I., Parks, D. W., and Neill, M. L., 1971, Associations between drinking water and death rates, in Hemphill, D. D., ed., Trace substances in environmental health—IV: Columbia, Univ. Missouri, p. 318–325.

Schroeder, H. A., 1960, Relation between mortality from cardiovascular disease and treated water supplies: Jour. Am. Med. Assoc., v. 172, p. 1902–1908.

——1966, Municipal drinking water and cardiovascular death rates: Jour. Am. Med. Assoc., v. 195, p. 81–85.

Shacklette, H. T., Sauer, H. I., and Miesch, A. T., 1970, Geochemical environments and cardiovascular mortality rates in Georgia: U.S. Geol. Survey Prof. Paper 574–C, 39 p.

——1972, Distribution of trace elements in the environment and the occurrence of heart disease in Georgia: Geol. Soc. America Bull., v. 83, p. 1077–1082.

U.S. Department of Agriculture, 1967, Soil survey laboratory data and descriptions for some soils of Indiana: Soil Survey Inv., rept. no. 18, 123 p.

Winton, E. F., and McCabe, L. J., 1969, Studies of water mineralization and health: Water Conditioning, v. 11, no. 9, p. 12–18.

MANUSCRIPT RECEIVED BY THE SOCIETY SEPTEMBER 19, 1973

Printed in U.S.A.

Geological Society of America
Special Paper 155
© 1975

Multivariate Relationships between Soil Composition and Human Mortality Rates in Missouri

Ronald R. Tidball
U.S. Geological Survey
Denver, Colorado 80225

AND

Herbert I. Sauer
Department of Community Health and Medical Practice
University of Missouri
Columbia, Missouri 65201

ABSTRACT

Premature death among humans in the state of Missouri appears to have little relation to the composition of soils in the vicinity of their usual residency. Our conclusion contrasts with a considerable part of the literature, which implies that soil is a factor affecting human health. The difference may arise either because people living in a given environment may not expose themselves in such a way as to be affected by the soil or because other important factors may overshadow the effect of soils.

Other studies have suggested a correlation between the incidence of either human disease or human mortality and soil characteristics. Most correlations have been of the simple bivariate type. The opportunity for a multivariate study has arisen only with the availability of chemical data on soils and mortality rates of humans from a common area.

The distribution of elements in Missouri soils exhibits some regional pattern, but mortality distribution patterns are not regionally distinct. Therefore, stepwise multiple regression is used to define possible subtle relationships. This multivariate search tool identifies which of the 32 elements measured in 1,140 soil samples collected throughout Missouri best relate to human mortality risk. Differences in age, sex, and race are closely associated with mortality risk; adjustments for these factors have been made by direct methods. There is a possibility that other factors, presently not recognized, need to be measured and controlled before dismissing the idea of a soil influence on mortality. We are continuing the search for such factors.

SOIL—A POOR MEASURE OF
PREMATURE HUMAN MORTALITY

Multiple regression analysis shows that the risk of premature death among humans in the State of Missouri has little relation to the composition of soils within the vicinity of their usual residency. The soil composition, expressed as total element concentration, serves here as an index of the chemical environment in which the people live. Soil may influence human mortality; that influence, however, may be masked if the people living in a given environment do not expose themselves in such a way as to be affected by the soil.

Each of the soil elements shown in the regression equations in Table 1 was selected by a stepwise procedure, and the elements that were not statistically significant were omitted. In total, the elements included in the equation explain only a small percentage of the total variance in the geographical distribution of the risk of premature death. This latter result is the basis of our conclusion in this study. The response curve relating mortality rate to the concentration of elements in the soil is probably not a simple linear function because most biological systems are concentration dependent. The response may differ markedly at either high or low concentrations from that occurring at more optimum concentrations. Therefore, we studied the mortality-environment system using a special case of the general linear model of regression, in which we examined the nonlinearity of the independent variables (chemical elements) by including both polynomial and nonpolynomial functions.

All of the regression equations for mortality among males contain, as independent variables, either one or both of the elements carbon and phosphorus, among others. The carbon is almost all organic. The terms are always positive for phosphorus (a detrimental effect) and always negative for carbon (a beneficial effect). These two elements are possible indicators of other aspects of the chemistry or other conditions in the soil. For example, carbon is significantly correlated at a probability level of 0.01 with the following elements: copper, iron, lithium, scandium, selenium, silicon (negative), and vanadium. Phosphorus is positively correlated at the same probability level (0.01) with the following elements: aluminum, calcium, magnesium, nickel, potassium, sodium, strontium, and zinc.

For unknown reasons, the combination of elements that enter the regression equations for females was entirely different from that found among males. Here boron, lithium, selenium, and zinc appear as independent variables with some regularity.

The relative importance of each independent variable in explaining the variance in the dependent variable may be estimated by comparing the absolute magnitudes of the normalized regression coefficients (Table 2). However, because some of the independent variables within any one regression equation are correlated to varying degrees (shown in Table 3), we shall interpret the normalized coefficients

TABLE 1. MULTIPLE REGRESSION EQUATIONS

Dependent variable	Independent variables	Percentage of total sum of squares of dependent variable explained
	Males	
All causes, logs	$= 3.09 - 0.137 \log C + 9.50\ P^2$	21
Major CV*, logs	$= 2.79 - 0.129 \log C + 0.247\ F^{1/2} + 7.58$	21
Coronary, logs	$= 2.60 + 6.28\ F^2 - 0.0084\ C^3 + 0.317$	19
Other major CV, logs	$= 2.41 + 0.23 \log Mn - 0.410 \log Y + 90.2$	21
Diabetes, arithmetic	$= 9{,}703 + 29.9 \log Cu - 0.0028\ Co^3 - 9{,}704\ e^{C/1000}$†	13
Malignant neoplasms, logs	$= 2.64 + 0.258 \log P - 0.013\ C^3 + 2.39(10^{-5})\ As^3$	19
	Females	
All causes, logs	$= 2.84 - 0.0029\ B + 0.110 \log Zn - 4.59(10^{-6})\ Li^3$	20
Major CV*, logs	$= 2.90 - 0.242 \log B + 0.167 \log Se + 0.145 \log Zn - 0.333\ Se^2 - 7.46(10^{-6})\ Li^3$	34
Coronary, logs	$= 2.18 - 0.165 \log C$	4
Other major CV, logs	$= 2.17 - 2.88(10^{-4})\ Zr - 0.166 \log C - 0.260 \log Co + 0.226 \log Mn + 0.142 \log Se - 0.512\ Se^3$	28
Diabetes, arithmetic	$= 2.51 - 924\ F^2$	4
Malignant neoplasms, logs	$=$ No significant regression	

Note: Equations identify significant (0.05 probability level) soil element terms (independent variables) that explain a percentage of the total variance in human mortality rates (dependent variable) according to cause of death among white males and females.

*CV means cardiovascular.

†e is the base of natural logarithms.

TABLE 2. NORMALIZED REGRESSION COEFFICIENTS

Dependent Variable	Independent Variables		
	Males		
All causes, logs	$-0.294 \log C$	$+0.392\ P^2$	
Major CV*, logs	$-0.268 \log C$	$+0.207\ F^{1/2}$	$+0.301\ P^2$
Coronary, logs	$+0.183\ F^2$	$-0.219\ C^3$	$+0.389\ Ca^3$
Other major CV, logs	$+0.441 \log Mn$	$-0.361 \log Y$	$+0.282\ P^3$
Diabetes, arithmetic	$+0.320 \log Cu$	$-0.182\ Co^3$	$-0.362\ e^{C/1000}$ †
Malignant neoplasms, logs	$+0.391 \log P$	$-0.329\ C^3$	$+0.197\ As^3$
	Females		
All causes, logs	$-0.262\ B$	$+0.295 \log Zn$	$-0.500\ Li^3$
Major CV*, logs	$-0.217 \log B$	$+0.632 \log Se$ $-0.634\ Se^2$	$+0.081 \log Zn$ $-0.585\ Li^3$
Coronary, logs	$-0.208 \log C$		
Other major CV, logs	$-0.299\ Zr$	$-0.238 \log C$ $+0.429 \log Mn$	$-0.292 \log Co$ $+0.406 \log Se$ $-0.477\ Se^3$
Diabetes, arithmetic	$-0.203\ F^2$		
Malignant neoplasms, logs	No significant regression		

Note: Equations indicate the relative weighting of each independent variable toward the prediction of mortality rates according to cause of death among white males and females. Coefficients pertain to the equations in Table 1.
*CV means cardiovascular.
†e is the base of natural logarithms.

in Table 2 only as approximate indicators of the relative contribution of each independent variable. Among males there are no important differences among the magnitudes of the coefficients. The largest coefficient is generally no more than double the smallest. Similarly, the coefficients are not greatly different among females, although lithium and selenium may explain more of the variance in the mortality rate than zinc and boron.

We find that soil carbon is only weakly related to the occurrence of malignant neoplasms among males and not related at all among females. This finding contrasts with some earlier work, where the organic-matter content of the soils in some English garden soils was related to the appearance of stomach cancer (Stocks and Davies, 1960, 1964). Voors (1970) reported a possible protective effect from lithium in drinking water against atherosclerotic heart disease. Although lithium was always included in the group of soil elements tested by multiple regression, it was never selected as having a statistically significant relationship with categories of any of the cardiovascular (CV) diseases. Our data suggest a beneficial effect from lithium on diseases from all causes and major CV among females, but only in association with other elements.

We hypothesize that people living on soils that have an abundance, but not necessarily an excess, of total elements should enjoy optimum health and longevity because of the low probability for either an element deficiency or toxicity. We might expect, therefore, that younger soils, with abundant total elements developed on glacial materials that dominate most of the northern half of Missouri and on the alluvium of the Missouri and Mississippi Rivers, would be associated with lower mortality rates. Further, we would expect soils with relatively smaller concentrations of most elements, developed on an older land surface in the southern part of Missouri, to be associated with higher mortality rates. Our results, as expressed by total element concentration in the soil, fail to support the hypothesis. Albrecht (1957) argued that the more fertile soils of the United States have the greater productive potential for protein, a desirable quality for the optimum nutrition of both animals and man. L. M. Hepple (quoted by Albrecht, 1957, p. 102–103) studied young men who had been called for military duty from Missouri by the Selective Service system; he suggested that better health could be expected among people living on the better soils. Shacklette and others (1970) found that soils with a higher concentration of total elements were associated with areas of lower CV mortality rates in Georgia. In contrast, however, Klusman and Sauer (1972) found that soils developed on glacial materials in Indiana, which have a more abundant natural supply of elements, were associated with higher CV mortality rates. Thus, nothing conclusive can be derived from these studies.

SOILS AND EPIDEMIOLOGY

Human diseases and mortalities have long been recognized to have a geographical distribution. Sauer and Donnell (1970) reported on the age and geographic differences in human mortality rates among white males in the United States. They observed that adjacent state-economic areas (a reporting unit of the U.S. Census Bureau) have positively correlated mortality rates and that the mortality rates of several age groups within a given location tend to be affected to a similar degree. These correlations suggest that local environment is an important determinant. The local environmental complex comprises the more obvious factors, such as the composition of soil, water, and food, in addition to other possible factors related to culture and pollution.

A review of studies done over the past century, particularly on cancer (Armstrong, 1962) and dental caries (Losee, 1962) among humans, indicates the popularity of the notion that soils play a role in the susceptibility for disease. Even today, investigators continue to identify the soil as related to a variety of diseases; yet, evidence is often circumstantial. That is, the incidence of the disease is geographically associated with soils of a particular composition or characteristic, but a specific causative factor is not identified.

Many diseases have been studied in this manner, some of which are as follows: consumption (tuberculosis) in England (Whitaker, 1869), gastric cancer in Japan (Segi and Kurihara, 1960), esophageal cancer among the Bantu people in the Transkei (Marais and Drewes, 1962), cancer in the Netherlands (Tromp and Diehl, 1955), stomach cancer associated with English garden soils (Stocks and Davies, 1960, 1964), multiple sclerosis in Finland (Salmi, 1963), amyotrophic lateral sclerosis in Japan (Morita and others, 1967), cardiovascular diseases in Georgia (Shacklette and others, 1970) and in Indiana (Klusman and Sauer, 1972), and dental caries in New Zealand (Cadell, 1962).

TABLE 3. CORRELATION COEFFICIENTS BETWEEN SOIL VARIABLES WHERE

Independent Variables	B	log B	C^3	log C	$e^{C/1000}$	log Co	log Cu
As^3	..	..	0.31	..	..	..	..
C^3	..	..	..	..	..	..	..
Log C	..	..	..	..	..	..	..
$e^{C/1000}$	..	..	..	..	..	..	0.25
Ca^3	..	..	0.41	..	..	..	..
Co^3	..	..	..	..	−0.11	..	0.14
Log Co	..	..	..	0.18	..	..	..
$F^{1/2}$	..	..	..	0.11	..	..	..
Li^3	−0.18	−0.16	..	..	..	..	..
Log Mn	..	..	..	−0.15	..	0.64	..
P^2	..	..	..	0.12	..	..	..
P^3	..	..	..	..	..	..	..
Se^2	..	−0.21	..	..	..	..	..
Se^3	..	..	..	0.42	..	0.01	..
Log Se	..	−0.23	..	0.49	..	0.07	..
Log Y	..	..	..	..	..	..	..
Log Zn	−0.08	−0.07	..	..	..	..	..

Studies based on circumstantial evidence are not without merit, however, because they can help to identify new directions for more definitive investigations. Few studies have been carried through to a definitive conclusion but the following study illustrates excellent experimentation.

Ludwig and others (1962) found that dental caries were more prevalent among children in New Zealand who resided on older alluvial soils than among another group of children who resided on younger saline soils. Although some studies might terminate at this point, the investigators extended their inquiry and determined that the composition of vegetables grown on the soils differed between the two areas, particularly in molybdenum concentration. This finding led to an important experiment that implicated molybdenum as a causative factor in dental caries. The ash of beans grown on each of the two soils was fed as a supplement to rats. The bean-ash from saline soils contained more molybdenum than that grown on the alluvial soils; the molybdenum provided a protective quality against caries in the rats. Similar results were found in South Africa (Pienaar and Bartel, 1968).

Proof of subtle disease-soil relations often requires a specific population or geographic area to ensure the absence of confounding factors. It is generally accepted that geographic patterns observed in endemic goiter are related to soil, food, or drinking water, but evidence linking the disease with local sources of iodine depends on the absence of supplements from outside the area. Endemic areas have been related to areas of iodine-deficient soils, particularly those remote from the sea coast (Karelina, 1961), or to remote areas where the inhabitants rely only on local foods (Besson et Paret, 1963). Goiter incidence decreased in parts of Europe following World War II as the distribution of foodstuffs with adequate iodine became wider (Mertz and others, 1967). However, not all goiter is directly dependent on iodine nutrition. Children in Tasmania who failed to

BOTH APPEAR AS TERMS WITHIN SAME REGRESSION EQUATION IN TABLE 1

F^2	log Mn	P^2	log P	Se^2	log Se	log Y	log Zn	Zr
..	..	..	0.06	..	..	..	..	..
0.09	..	..	0.29	..	..	..	..	..
..	−0.15	..	..	..	..	..	..	−0.17
..	..	..	..	..	..	..	..	..
0.25	..	..	..	..	..	..	..	..
..	..	..	..	..	..	..	..	..
..	..	..	..	..	..	..	..	0.27
..	..	0.34	..	..	..	..	..	..
..	..	..	..	0.60	0.67	..	0.56	..
..	..	..	..	..	..	0.49	..	0.38
..	..	..	..	..	..	..	..	..
..	−0.36	..	..	..	..	−0.26	..	..
..	..	..	..	..	0.88	..	0.32	..
..	−0.18	..	..	..	0.79	..	..	−0.28
..	−0.26	..	..	..	..	..	..	−0.28
..	0.49	..	..	..	..	..	..	..
..	..	..	..	..	0.43	..	..	..

respond to iodine supplement had acquired an antithyroid substance (hexuronic acid) that was transmitted from cabbage through cow's milk (Marine and others, 1933). The concentration of hexuronic acid in the cabbage varied according to season and climate rather than to soil. This study does not necessarily discredit the effect of iodine on goiter in the general case, but rather, it recognizes that some more dominant factor controls the behavior of thyroid in these special circumstances. The study emphasizes the need for a thorough investigation.

Armstrong (1964) discussed the reliability of soil, plant, and water composition as trace-element indicators of the human diet. He concluded that analyses of source materials alone are probably an unsuitable predictor of human exposure because of the intervention of physical and cultural factors between the origin of trace elements and the point of food consumption. The validity of conclusions based on chemical analyses that measure the *total* element concentrations, rather than *available* forms of the elements in soil, also has been questioned (Voisin, 1959, p. 26; Dvoyrin, 1968, p. 560). A suitable measure of forms of availability is difficult to establish and this perhaps explains why several previous studies on soil-health relationships have been based on "total" analyses. Nevertheless, every opportunity to search for relationships should be utilized. Thus, with the combination of a large data bank on soils and human mortality rates for the state of Missouri, we examined their relationship on a multivariate basis with the realization that the risk of premature death may be affected by two or more elements simultaneously.

The relationship between the mortality rate for a specific cause (dependent variable) and several soil element concentrations (independent variables) is evaluated by stepwise multiple regression. A brief discussion of the mortality data is given, followed by a description of the soils data. Finally, the multiple regression method is described.

MORTALITY RATES

A special tabulation of the number of human deaths for the 10-yr period 1950 through 1959 was made by the Missouri State Division of Health in accord with our specifications. These tabulations are by county of usual residence, by age, by sex, and by race for selected causes of death—all causes (including accidents); all major cardiovascular (CV) diseases, which are subdivided into coronary heart disease and other CV; diabetes; and malignant neoplasms (cancer). Some mortality rates based on these tabulations have been published (Sauer and others, 1964). A number of checks were made of various subtotals with the counts of the National Office of Vital Statistics (now the National Center for Health Statistics); there was a high degree of agreement, the differences in the counts being generally about 0.5 percent.

The population at risk was estimated from arithmetic interpolation of the population counts from official sources (U.S. Census Bureau, 1952, 1963), and specific age-sex-race rates were calculated for age groups 35 to 44, 45 to 54, 55 to 64, and 65 to 74 years. From these rates, age-adjusted rates were calculated by the direct method using the total United States population in those age groups in 1950 as the standard population (Linder and Grove, 1943). Mortality rates are expressed as the average annual number of deaths per 100,000 people in the specified age-sex-race group.

All rates used in the correlations are for whites only, because for most counties in Missouri the population of "other races" is so small that chance fluctuation would make mortality rates almost meaningless. Individuals with Mexican surnames are routinely classified as white, but in Missouri their numbers are so small that they do not appreciably affect the rates, even though Mexican males have lower death rates in middle age than do other whites. Other ethnic groups of whites are small enough to make only a minor contribution to geographic differences in mortality rates.

The mortality rates thus calculated for whites by sex and age constitute a measure of the risk of premature death—"premature" in the sense that death occurred between age 35 to 74, in middle age or "early old age" rather than after age 75. This rate is presented as the most objective, most tangible measure of health now available.

SOIL MATERIALS

Soil samples were collected throughout the state of Missouri as part of a regional environmental evaluation of the state (Connor and others, 1972). A total of 1,140 samples were collected from agricultural soils at the rate of 10 samples per county. Each specimen represents a composite of numerous specimens collected from the surface horizon (0 to 15 cm depth) throughout a selected field. After collection, the entire sample set was arranged in a randomized sequence for all laboratory preparation and analysis. This procedure effectively transforms any systematic laboratory error into a random error so that interpretations of any trends in the data are not confounded by laboratory error. Each specimen was gently disaggregated and sieved through a 2-mm stainless-steel screen. The material that passed through the screen was ground in a ceramic mill to −100 mesh and was thoroughly mixed before analysis. The specimens were air dried at less than 30° C.

CHEMICAL ANALYSIS OF SOILS

The laboratory procedures used to determine total element content have been described elsewhere (U.S. Geol. Survey, 1972, p. 4–9). The semiquantitative spectrographic method used was the same as that described by Myers and others (1961), except that the analytical results are reported in six steps per order of magnitude rather than three. The spectrographic method was used to scan for 60 elements, but less than one-half of these elements occur in concentrations above the lower limit of determination. Therefore, where the spectrographic analysis was inadequate, other methods were used: atomic absorption spectrophotometry for lithium, magnesium, mercury, sodium, and zinc; specific-ion electrode for fluorine; spectrophotometric-isotope dilution for arsenic; and x-ray fluorescence for aluminum, calcium, iron, phosphorus, potassium, selenium, and silicon. Selenium analysis was preceded by a chemical separation using a tellurium carrier. Emission spectrography was used for barium, boron, chromium, cobalt, copper, gallium, lanthanum, lead, manganese, nickel, scandium, strontium, titanium, vanadium, ytterbium, yttrium, and zirconium. Carbon was measured gasometrically.

DISTRIBUTION OF COUNTY MEANS

The mortality rates are expressed as average annual death rates per 100,000 population exposed to risk and thus are county means. Counties are the smallest administrative units for which we are able to calculate rates; because a major part of the population of a county usually resides near the center of the county, the county seems to be a useful unit for such study. The soils data were collected within counties and have been summarized as county means to conform with the mortality rates.

The distributions of mortality rates from major CV diseases among males and females by counties are shown in Figures 1 and 2. These distribution maps were selected to illustrate the lack of a broad geographic pattern over the region and the weak consistency between sexes. In fact, the mortality data are so homogeneous among counties that it would be difficult to find any important associations with other environmental variables. Note from the mean and range on the histograms in Figures 1 and 2 that the risk of premature death from major CV diseases among males is more than double that among females. Mortality rates for various causes have been tabulated by counties and published elsewhere (Sauer and others, 1964, 1973, 1974).

Statewide patterns in the mortality data (Figs. 1 and 2) are much less distinct than the patterns of some selected soil elements (Figs. 3 through 5). A complete tabulation of soil means by counties was published elsewhere (Tidball, 1974).

Soil element distribution conforms more or less to the distribution of major parent-material types, and therefore, distinctive differences tend to occur between

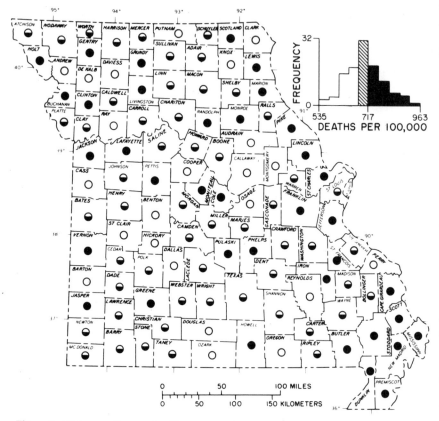

Figure 1. Major cardiovascular disease mortality rates among white males in Missouri. Rates express deaths per 100,000 people as county averages. Solid dots on the map represent the highest of the three concentration classes on the histogram; open circles represent the lowest class. Values on the abscissa are the minimum, the geometric mean, and the maximum, respectively.

one region and another. Approximately the northern half of the state has been glaciated. Geologically young soils have developed on these glacial materials (till and loess) and on the alluvium in the Missouri and Mississippi River valleys, which is probably heavily affected by glacial outwash sediments. The soils of glacially affected areas have larger concentrations of many trace elements than do the soils in most of the southern half of the state (Tidball, 1972a, 1972b).

The soils in the south rest on a much older land surface, on which the predominant parent material is deeply weathered carbonate-rock residuum, with smaller areas on sandstone and shale parent materials. Some minimum quantity of loess may be incorporated in the topsoil but not in sufficient quantity to mask the influence of the underlying parent material.

Soil pH was not measured on these samples. However, data from samples collected from the surface horizon (0 to 15 cm depth) at 115 sites on cultivated soils of Missouri showed no significant regional variation (J. A. Erdman, 1974,

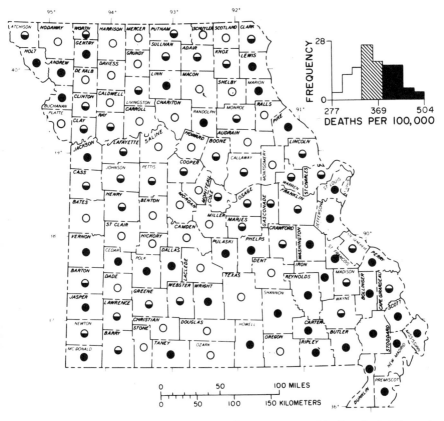

Figure 2. Major cardiovascular disease mortality rates among white females in Missouri. Rates express deaths per 100,000 people as county averages. Solid dots on the map represent the highest of the three concentration classes on the histogram; open circles represent the lowest class. Values on the abscissa are the minimum, the geometric mean, and the maximum, respectively.

oral commun.). The average pH is 6.4; the 95 percent expected range is 4.8 to 7.9. Soil pH may affect the availability of various soil elements to plants and animals; if it does, the influence of pH should be no greater in one part of the state than in another part.

STEPWISE MULTIPLE REGRESSION

Because the distribution patterns among both the mortality rates and the soil elements are not visually comparable, we resorted to a multivariate statistical technique, multiple regression, which aids in identifying more subtle relationships. One of the more usual applications of regression is to predict the response of a dependent variable that is known to be influenced by the simultaneous effects of one or more known independent variables. We apply multiple regression, however, more as a search technique to identify which combination of many

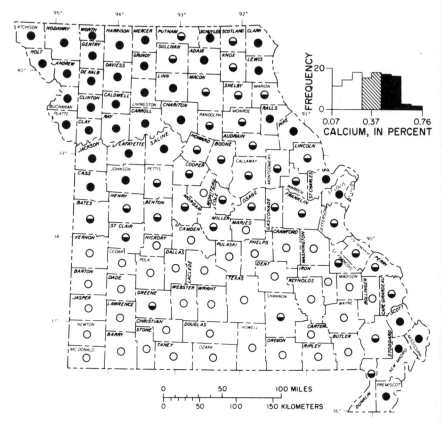

Figure 3. Calcium concentration in the surface horizon (0 to 15 cm depth) of agricultural soils of Missouri. Map symbols express concentrations as county averages. Solid dots represent the highest of the three concentration classes on the histogram; open circles represent the lowest class. Values on the abscissa are the minimum, the arithmetic mean, and the maximum, respectively.

independent variables available for testing best explains the observed variation in the dependent variable. This application is called "stepwise regression."

The method of stepwise regression used is similar to the one given by Efroymsen (1960) but slightly modified as described by Miesch and Connor (1968, p. 3–4). The general model is

$$Y = \alpha + \beta_1 X_1 + \beta_2 X_2 + \ldots \beta_k X_k + \epsilon, \tag{1}$$

where Y, the county mortality rate or some simple transformation thereof, is a response that is, in part, linearly dependent on one or more of the variables designated by X. The Xs are, in this case, average concentrations or simple functions of these averages, Z, of chemical constituents in 10 soil samples from a given county; each X is adjusted by a regression coefficient, β. The regression constant, α, is the intercept of the regression curve with the Y axis when all of the X terms

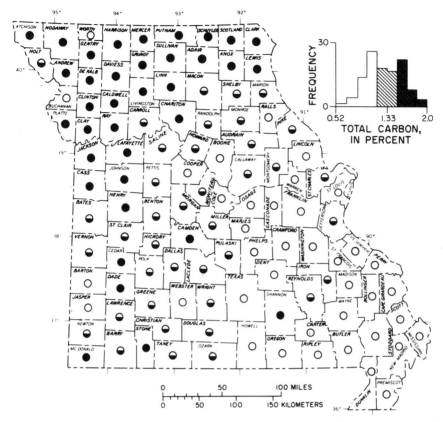

Figure 4. Total carbon concentration in the surface horizon (0 to 15 cm depth) of agricultural soils of Missouri. Map symbols express concentrations as county averages. Solid dots represent the highest of the three concentration classes on the histogram; open circles represent the lowest class. Values on the abscissa are the minimum, the arithmetic mean, and the maximum, respectively.

equal zero. The variable ε is that portion of the mortality rate that cannot be described by the regression equation (Table 1). The functions of X that are tested include the following: $X = Z, Z^{1/2}, Z^2, Z^3, \log Z,$ and $e^{(Z/1000)}$, where e is the base of natural logarithms.

The following 32 chemical elements were considered in this investigation: aluminum, arsenic, barium, boron, calcium, carbon, chromium, cobalt, copper, fluorine, gallium, iron, lanthanum, lead, lithium, magnesium, manganese, mercury, nickel, phosphorus, potassium, scandium, selenium, silicon, sodium, strontium, titanium, vanadium, ytterbium, yttrium, zinc, and zirconium. The total number of functions of Z eligible to enter each of the computed regression equations was 192.

The stepwise procedure used to select variables is of the step-up variety in the classification of procedures used by Snedecor and Cochran (1967, p. 413). The first variable entered is the one that has the highest linear correlation with

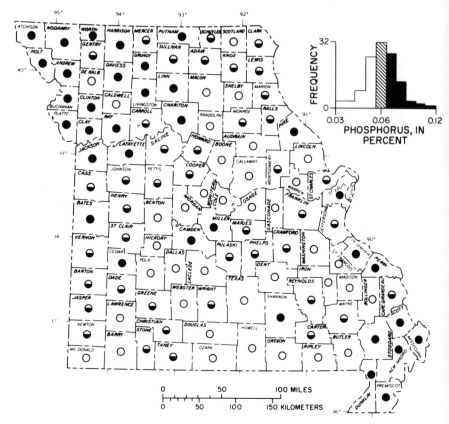

Figure 5. Phosphorus concentration in the surface horizon (0 to 15 cm depth) of agricultural soils of Missouri. Map symbols express concentrations as county averages. Solid dots represent the highest of the three concentration classes on the histogram; open circles represent the lowest class. Values on the abscissa are the minimum, the geometric mean, and the maximum, respectively.

the dependent variable, Y. The standardized partial regression coefficients of the other independent variables are then examined and the variable having the highest coefficient is added to the regression equation. Each time a variable is added to the equation, all variables in the equation are tested for statistical significance at the 0.05 level. Those found not to account for significant reductions in the variance of Y are deleted. The procedure continues until all variables in the equation are significant and all those outside are not. Of the 192 variables eligible to enter the equation in each regression computation, no more than six ever did enter.

The initial estimates of the β_k in equation (1), derived by the regression procedure, are designated by b'_k. These initial estimates are in normalized form and are applicable where both Y and the Xs are expressed in units of standard deviation from the mean. The coefficients applicable when Y and the Xs are given in the original units of measurement are derived by

$$b_k = \frac{b'_k S_y}{S_k},$$ (2)

where S_y and S_k are the standard deviations of Y and X_k, respectively. The estimate, a, of the regression constant, α, in equation (1) is given by

$$a = \bar{Y} - \Sigma\,(b_k\,\bar{X}_k),$$ (3)

where $\bar{Y}$ and $\bar{X}_k$ are the arithmetic means of Y and X_k.

The derived regression equations containing the normalized coefficients, b'_k (sometimes called standardized partial regression coefficients), are given in Table 2. Equations containing the final regression coefficients, b_k, which are estimates of the β_k in equation (1), are given in Table 1.

The coefficients, b_k, are used to estimate the response, Y, from knowledge of the Xs. The b_ks are thought to be the best estimates that can be obtained by means of conventional statistical procedures. Snedecor and Cochran (1967, p. 394–397) have shown, however, that coefficients of this sort may be biased to some undeterminable degree when the regression equation does not contain all the independent variables that are related to the dependent variable. Inasmuch as the mortality rates examined here are possibly related to other factors in addition to soil chemistry, it must follow that the estimated coefficients are indeed biased to an unknown degree. We accept the estimates as the best we can obtain, but awareness of the bias will prohibit us from using them in any attempt to place limits on, or recommend standards for, tolerable ranges of soil chemistry.

The relative importance of each independent variable in explaining the variance in the mortality rates may be evaluated by comparing the absolute magnitude of the normalized coefficients, b'_k. However, inasmuch as some of the independent variables within any one regression equation are linearly related to varying degrees (see correlation coefficients in Table 3), we shall use the normalized coefficients as only crude indicators of the relative strengths of the relations that each independent variable has to the corresponding mortality rate.

NEW DIRECTIONS

The success of future studies of the relation between soils and human morbidity or human mortality may require a further refinement of data compilation before a valid understanding emerges. A review (Armstrong, 1962) of the etiology of cancer in England during the latter part of the 19th century described the notion that certain locales were recognized as "cancer galleys," "cancer houses," or even "cancer rooms" within a house. In some instances, the house or the bedding was destroyed and thereafter the disease disappeared. Consequently, people believed that evil spirits were responsible, because once these spirits were "driven out" the problem vanished. The superstition of the "cancer house" was finally discredited in the early 1930s by statistical studies based on very careful experimental designs that exposed the influence of the "house" as an artifact. Thereafter, the investigator was free to develop a new epidemiological model to guide his inquiries. This example illustrates, first, the error in adopting the wrong model and, second, the futility in trying to explain the observations in the light of that model.

The variation in human mortality rates among Missouri counties is small. It is possible that the county compilation procedure fails to assemble mortality data in a way that best emphasizes geographic differences. Although differences in the soils among counties are more evident than the variation in human mortality rates, political divisions are no substitute for an appropriate natural grouping of soils with common chemical attributes.

Investigators continue to identify certain geographic factors that indicate something in the environment as a determinant in the incidence of a human disease. Indeed, convincing evidence from studies of diseases among livestock supports the hypothesis that soil can have a direct influence on health. There are a number of factors that influence geographic differences in mortality rates, and the interactions of these factors are undoubtedly complex. If soils (and geology) do cause differences in mortality rates, their influence may be direct, through factors such as the following: the composition of drinking water and locally grown food, contamination from airborne and waterborne dust, organic compounds, and radioactive substances. However, soil influences also may be indirect. For example, growth of many types of crops on a fertile soil might be impractical on an infertile soil. Thus, the soil may indirectly affect the type of socioeconomic activity that is efficient for the area; and in turn, this activity may affect the mortality risk either positively or negatively. A study of 92 large metropolitan areas of the United States showed that 81 percent of the variance in mortality caused by CV diseases for white females was associated principally with socioeconomic factors (Sauer, 1974). The soil may also be optimum for a variety of pathogenic organisms that could foster an association between the soil and human disease.

We established a limited relationship between the risk of premature death and soil composition, based on the definition of these variables used in this study. There is a possibility that we need to measure and control other factors both in the population at risk and in the characteristics of the soils, which we presently have not recognized.

ACKNOWLEDGMENTS

The statewide staff of the Extension Division of the University of Missouri, under the direction of Walter F. Heidlage, Program Coordinator, Extension Environmental Health, collected most of the soil specimens. Chemical analysis of all specimens was done in the laboratories of the U.S. Geological Survey in Denver, Colorado, and in Reston, Virginia. The principal methods of analyses were the semiquantitative spectrography by L. A. Bradley and x-ray fluorescence by J. S. Wahlberg, M. W. Solt, and Mike Brown. Other analyses for individual elements were performed by the following personnel: Johnnie Gardner, magnesium and sodium; I. C. Frost, G. T. Burrow, and G. D. Shipley, carbon; J. P. Cahill, cadmium; J. A. Thomas, lithium and zinc; and R. L. Turner, mercury. Josephine G. Boerngen assisted in the automatic data processing. French, German, and Russian papers were translated by Dorothy B. Vitaliano.

Deaths for 1950 through 1959 were tabulated and rates calculated under the direction of W. W. Marshall, Jr., formerly Director of Statistical Activities, Missouri State Division of Health.

REFERENCES CITED

Albrecht, W. A., 1957, Soil fertility and biotic geography: Geog. Rev., v. 47, p. 86–105.

Armstrong, R. W., 1962, Cancer and soil—Review and counsel: Prof. Geographer, v. 14, no. 3, p. 7–13.

——1964, Environmental factors involved in studying the relationship between soil elements and disease: Am. Jour. Public Health, v. 54, no. 9, p. 1536–1544.

Besson et Paret, Albert, 1963, Incidence de la composition de sol sur la santé de l'homme et sa nutrition (Effect of the composition of the soil on the health of man and his nutrition): Acad. d'Agriculture, Comptes Rendus Hebdomadaires des Séances, v. 49, p. 1093–1099.

Cadell, P. B., 1962, Prevalence of dental caries in relation to New Zealand soils, in Neale, G. J., ed., Transactions of joint meeting of Commissions IV and V: Internat. Soc. Soil Sci., Nov. 13–22, 1962, p. 884–888.

Connor, J. J., Feder, G. L., Erdman, J. A., and Tidball, R. R., 1972, Environmental geochemistry in Missouri—A multidisciplinary study: Internat. Geol. Cong., 24th, Montreal, Canada 1972, Symp. I, p. 7–14.

Dvoyrin, V. V., 1968, Geochemical aspects of the epidemiology of malignancies: Neoplasma, v. 15, no. 5, p. 559–564.

Efroymsen, M. A., 1960, Multiple regression analysis, in Ralston, Anthony, and Wilf, H. S., eds., Mathematical methods for digital computers: New York, John Wiley & Sons, Inc., p. 191–203.

Karelina, L. V., 1961, (Iodine in the soils of the Latvian S.S.R. in connection with the distribution of endemic goiter, trans.): Latvijas Padomju Socialistiskas Republikas Zinatnu Akad., Lab. Biokhim. Pochv i Mikroelementov, Trudy Lab. biokhim. pochv mikroelementov (Mikroelementy i Urozhai), v. 3, p. 233–255.

Klusman, R. W., and Sauer, H. I., 1972, Some possible relationships of water and soil chemistry to cardiovascular diseases in Indiana: Geol. Soc. America, Abs. with Programs, v. 7, no. 4, p. 563–564.

Linder, F. E., and Grove, R. D., 1943, Vital statistics rates in the United States, 1900–1940: Washington, D.C., U.S. Govt. Printing Office, 1051 p.

Losee, F. L., 1962, Soils and human health, with particular reference to dental health, in Neale, G. J., ed., Transactions of joint meeting of Commissions IV and V: Internat. Soc. Soil Sci., Nov. 13–22, 1962, p. 889–894.

Ludwig, T. G., Healy, W. B., and Malthus, R. S., 1962, Dental caries prevalence in specific soil areas at Napier and Hastings, in Neale, G. J., ed., Transactions of joint meeting of Commissions IV and V: Internat. Soc. Soil Sci., Nov. 13–22, 1962, p. 895–903.

Marais, J.A.H., and Drewes, E.F.R., 1962, The relationship between solid geology and oesophageal cancer distribution in the Transkei: South Africa Geol. Survey Annals, v. 1, p. 105–118.

Marine, David, Baumann, E. J., Webster, Bruce, and Cipra, Anna, 1933, Occurrence of antigoitrous substances in plants: Jour. Experimental Medicine, v. 57, p. 121–137.

Mertz, D. P., Sarre, H., Schwoerer, P., and Meigen, B., 1967, Über den Einfluss des Wohlstandes auf die Häufigkeit und die Verteilung des endemischen Kropfes in Südbaden (On the effect of prosperity on the frequency and distribution of endemic goiter in southern Baden): Verh. Deutsch Gesell. Innere Medizin, v. 73, p. 379–383.

Miesch, A. T., and Connor, J. J., 1968, Stepwise regression and nonpolynomial models in trend analysis: Kansas Geol. Survey Computer Contr. 27, 40 p.

Morita, Shuji, Hattori, Tomoo, and Aoki, Akira, 1967, Medico-pedological studies on endemics—Chemical composition of soils in relation to amyotrophic lateral sclerosis in Kii Peninsula, Japan: Soil Sci. and Plant Nutrition, v. 13, no. 2, p. 45–52.

Myers, A. T., Havens, R. G., and Dunton, P. J., 1961, A spectrochemical method for the semiquantitative analysis of rocks, minerals, and ores: U.S. Geol. Survey Bull. 1084–I p. 207–229.

Pienaar, W. J., and Bartel, E. E., 1968, Molybdenum content of vegetables and soils from the Vredendal and Langkloof areas: Jour. Dental Assoc. South Africa, v. 23, no. 8, p. 242–244.

Salmi, Martii, 1963, On relations between geology and multiple sclerosis: Acta Geographica v. 17, no. 4, p. 1–13.

Sauer, H. I., 1974, Relationship between trace element content of the drinking water and chronic diseases: Water Quality Conf., 16th, Proc., Illinois Univ., Urbana, Feb. 1974 *in* Water Quality Conf., 16th, Proc.: Feb. 12–13, 1974, p. 39–48.

Sauer, H. I., and Donnell, H. D., Jr., 1970, Age and geographic differences in death rates: Jour. Gerontology, v. 25, no. 2, p. 83–86.

Sauer, H. I., Banta, J. E., and Marshall, W. W., Jr., 1964, Cardiovascular diseases mortality patterns among middle-aged white males in Missouri: Missouri Medicine, v. 61, Nov., p. 921–926, 929.

Sauer, H. I., Marshall, W. W., and Valiunas, L. S., 1973, Death rates for all causes, age 35–74, by sex and race, 1950–1959 and 1959–1969: Columbia, Missouri Univ., Data for Missouri, Health and Medical Sec., Extension Div., p. 7800.

Sauer, H. I., Wright, H. T., and Land, G. H., 1974, Death rates for cardiovascular diseases, whites age 35–74 by sex, 1950–1972: Columbia, Missouri Univ., Data for Missouri, Health and Medical Sec., Extension Div., p. 7801.

Segi, Mitsuo, and Kurihara, Minoru, 1960, Cancer in Japan from the viewpoint of geographical pathology: Tohoku Jour. Experimental Medicine, v. 72, p. 169–193.

Shacklette, H. T., Sauer, H. I., and Miesch, A. T., 1970, Geochemical environments and cardiovascular mortality rates in Georgia: U.S. Geol. Survey Prof. Paper 574–C, 39 p.

Snedecor, G. W., and Cochran, W. G., 1967, Statistical methods [6th ed.]: Ames, Iowa State Univ. Press, 593 p.

Stocks, P., and Davies, R. I., 1960, Epidemiological evidence from chemical and spectrographic analyses that soil is concerned in the causation of cancer: British Jour. Cancer, v. 14, p. 8–22.

——1964, Zinc and copper content of soils associated with the incidence of cancer of the stomach and other organs: British Jour. Cancer, v. 18, p. 14–24.

Tidball, R. R., 1972a, Geochemical survey of soils, *in* Geochemical survey of Missouri—Plans and progress for fifth six-month period (July–December 1971): U.S. Geol. Survey Open-File Rept., p. 41–55.

——1972b, Geochemical survey of soils, *in* Geochemical survey of Missouri—Plans and progress for sixth six-month period (January–June 1972): U.S. Geol. Survey Open-File Rept., p. 19–57.

——1974, Average composition of agricultural soils in Missouri counties: U.S. Geol. Survey Open-File Rept. 74–66, 25 p.

Tromp, S. W., and Diehl, J. C., 1955, A statistical study of the possible relationship between cancer of the stomach and soil: British Jour. Cancer, v. 9, no. 3, p. 349–357.

U.S. Census Bureau, 1952, Characteristics of population, number of inhabitants, general and detailed characteristics of population, Vol. 2 of Missouri, Pt. 25, of Census of population, 1950: Washington, D.C., U.S. Govt. Printing Office, 304 p.

——1963, Characteristics of population, number of inhabitants, general population characteristics, general social and economic characteristics, and detailed characteristics, Vol. 2 of Missouri, Pt. 27, of Census of population, 1960: Washington, D.C., U.S. Govt. Printing Office, 588 p.

U.S. Geological Survey, 1972, Geochemical survey of Missouri—Plans and progress for second six-month period (January–June 1970): U.S. Geol. Survey Open-File Rept., 60 p.

Voisin, Andre, 1959, Soil, grass and cancer: New York, Philos. Library, Inc., 302 p. (trans. from French by Herriot, C.T.M., and Kennedy, Henry).

Voors, A. W., 1970, Lithium in the drinking water and atherosclerotic heart death—Epidemiologic argument for protective effect: Am. Jour. Epidemiology, v. 92, no. 3, p. 164–171.

Whitaker, William, 1869, On the connection of the geological structure and the physical features of the south-east of England, with the consumption death-rate: Geol. Mag. London, v. 6, no. 65, p. 499–505.

Paper Presented at the 1972 Annual Meeting of the Geological Society of America in Minneapolis, Minnesota
Manuscript Received by the Society September 17, 1973
Revised Manuscript Received September 23, 1974

Printed in U.S.A.

Geological Society of America
Special Paper 155
© 1975

The Molybdenum Project: Geochemical Aspects

DONALD D. RUNNELLS
Department of Geological Sciences
University of Colorado
Boulder, Colorado 80302

WILLARD R. CHAPPELL
Department of Physics and Astrophysics
University of Colorado
Boulder, Colorado 80302

AND

ROBERT MEGLEN
The Molybdenum Project
University of Colorado
Boulder, Colorado 80302

ABSTRACT

An interdisciplinary group of faculty from the University of Colorado and from Colorado State University is studying molybdenum in the environment. Molybdenum plays an essential role in the nitrogen cycle of plants and may cause disturbance of copper metabolism in animals. The world's largest molybdenum-producing mine is at Climax, Colorado. Rivers in Colorado exhibit some of the highest reported concentrations of molybdenum in the United States. Colorado offers a model system for the study of the release and effect of molybdenum.

The geochemistry of molybdenum is complex. The principal dissolved form of the metal in natural waters is an anion, MoO_4^{--}. At values of pH below about 6, the bimolybdate ion, $HMoO_4^-$, becomes dominant. The bimolybdate ion is relatively immobile in natural systems at low pH, probably because of adsorption or coprecipitation on metal hydroxides. In the acid soils of the alpine environment of Colorado, molybdenum forms a well-defined halo of elevated concentrations around a mineralized, undisturbed zone in the bedrock. We have attempted to

61

define a natural datum or background level of molybdenum in the vicinity of the undisturbed mineralized zone and to compare the concentrations of molybdenum in the undisturbed area to those present in the vicinity of mines and mills in the same mountainous area. Such a comparison is extremely difficult and tenuous because of differences in drainage and glaciation between the two areas.

INTRODUCTION

The Molybdenum Project at the University of Colorado is an interdisciplinary study group consisting of twelve faculty (eight from the University of Colorado and four from Colorado State University). The disciplines represented are geochemistry, physics, civil engineering, biochemistry, biology, animal sciences, agronomy, and epidemiology. The group first formed in the fall of 1970 and was initially funded by a small grant from the University of Colorado. Since June 1971, the study has been supported by the R.A.N.N. division of the National Science Foundation.

The long-range goals of the study involve answering three basic questions: (1) What are the effects of the release of molybdenum on the environment and public health? (2) If these effects warrant action by the populations affected, what are some of the available alternatives? (3) Which alternatives or actions—such as effluent standards, water quality standards, water resource management, farm management, and wildlife management—are the most reasonable approaches for reducing existing or potential hazards?

Molybdenum has been of interest to agricultural scientists for the last few decades. It is a widely studied metal because at low levels it plays an essential role in the nitrogen cycle of plants (Sauchelli, 1969), while at higher levels in forage it leads to a disturbance of copper metabolism in several species of animals, particularly ruminants (Underwood, 1971). It occurs in animals as an integral part of such enzymes as xanthine oxidase, aldehyde oxidase, and sulfite oxidase (Cohen and others, 1971).

Molybdenum has been established as the cause of a long-recognized disease of ruminants known variously as "teartness," "peat scours," or "alkalied." This disease, now commonly referred to as "molybdenosis," leads to severe diarrhea, loss of appetite, discoloration of hair, joint abnormalities, osteoporosis, lack of sexual interest, and, occasionally, death. The lowest concentrations in forage at which symptoms have become evident is 5 ppm. Because an interference with copper metabolism is involved, the level of copper is important in determining the toxic level of molybdenum. For normal copper levels, 15 ppm is a widely accepted value for the concentration of molybdenum in forage needed to produce clinical symptoms in the animals grazing the forage (Kubota and others, 1961). Considerable work has been done on the effects of molybdenum on guinea pigs, rats, and rabbits. In all these species there is a noticeable antagonism between copper and molybdenum. However, some species are much less sensitive than others. Molybdenum is most toxic to ruminants and least toxic to rats, with rabbits and guinea pigs in an intermediate range. The symptoms also differ according to the species, although most species suffer from some disturbance of the bone metabolism.

Molybdenum occurs on the average as about 1 to 2 ppm of the Earth's crust.

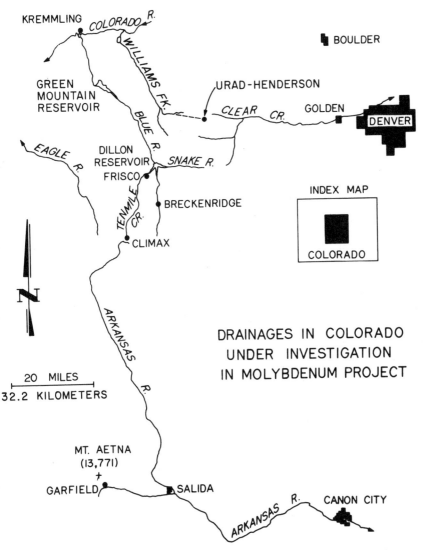

Figure 1. Index map of Colorado. Locations of drainages and study sites.

The world's largest molybdenum-producing mine is at Climax, Colorado (see Fig. 1). This mine produces about 60 percent of the molybdenum mined in the United States. A smaller mine is located near Idaho Springs, Colorado (the Urad mine), and preparations are being made to mine the Henderson deposit (near Urad; Fig. 1). The Henderson deposit promises to be about the same size as Climax (Clark, 1972). These operations all involve molybdenite MoS_2 as the primary ore. Sources of growing importance are porphyry copper mines that produce molybdenum as a by-product.

The release of molybdenum also occurs from sources other than molybdenum mining and milling. The possibility that power plants fired with fossil fuels can be a significant source is an area of active investigation. The mining and milling of uranium is another potential source (Christianson, 1970). The porphyry copper mines mentioned above present another possible source.

Water is the principal method of transport away from sources. Although the average value for United States surface waters was found to be 0.68 ppb (Hem, 1970), Kopp and Kroner (1967) in their study of key points along the major drainage basins of the United States found that 38 stations recorded a maximum level higher than 100 ppb and 26 stations recorded mean concentrations greater than 50 ppb. Of the four stations recording the highest levels, three were in Colorado and one was just across the Kansas border. Because the water in these rivers originates in Colorado, the state provides an interesting model system for a study of molybdenum release and transport in the environment.

The research plan consists of four major parts that are interrelated and directed toward answering the questions posed by the long-range goals mentioned above. These four areas of concern are (1) ecological effects and transport in natural and disturbed areas; (2) investigation of the water-soil-forage-cow-milk food chain; (3) analytical facilities and research; and (4) metabolic and physiological effects.

The study of ecological effects and transport in natural and disturbed areas involves the investigation of the molybdenum levels in soils, plants, stream sediments, water, and animals in areas of active mining (Climax and Urad) and an area in Colorado where an exposed molybdenum deposit is not being mined (Mount Aetna; Fig. 1). The purpose is to investigate the levels of molybdenum being cycled through the environment and to understand what portion is due to human activity and what portion is due to natural processes, such as weathering.

The investigation of the water-soil-forage-cow-milk food chain is motivated by the known toxic effects on cattle and sheep. The Federal Water Pollution Control Administration (1968, p. 154; now known as the Federal Water Quality Administration) suggested a tolerance limit of 5 ppb dissolved molybdenum in irrigation water for most soils, with an upper limit of 50 ppb for intermittent use on acid soils. This suggested standard is based on the work of Kubota and others (1963) on the effect of the moisture content of soil on the uptake of molybdenum by alsike clover. The plant and soil scientists in our group are developing tests for available molybdenum in soils and are conducting extensive field and laboratory investigations in order to establish the information needed to develop irrigation-water standards. In addition, we are carrying out studies to determine the transport of molybdenum into milk.

The quality of many of the results depends on the quality of the analytical laboratories. The standard methods (colorimetric and atomic absorption) are used, and a relatively new modification of the x-ray fluorescence method using solid-state detectors and charged particle excitation has been developed.

Biologists and biochemists in the group are carrying out extensive investigations of the metabolic and physiological effects.

The story begins, however, with the initial release and transport of molybdenum away from the source. The understanding of this aspect is tied to the understanding of the geochemistry of molybdenum. The purpose of this paper is to present some of the preliminary results that relate specifically to geochemistry.

GEOCHEMISTRY

Molybdenum is unusual among the metals in that its dominant dissolved form is an anion, MoO_4^{--}. In this mode of occurrence it is similar to arsenic and selenium, but it is different from such cationic species as zinc, copper, cadmium, lead, and others. Titley and Anthony (1961) and Hansuld (1966) concluded that, below a pH of about 6, the bimolybdate ion $HMoO_4^-$ becomes the dominant dissolved species under most conditions. In this acidic form, molybdenum is relatively immobile in natural weathering environments (Hansuld, 1966, Fig. 6, p. 77).

At least part of the reason for the immobility of molybdenum at low values of pH is that $HMoO_4^-$ is readily adsorbed or coprecipitated with the hydroxides of such metals as aluminum and iron. Jones (1957) showed that a large portion of dissolved molybdenum could be removed from aqueous solution by precipitates of aluminum hydroxide and iron hydroxide at pH values from about 2.5 to 7. Bhappu and others (1965) and Pérez (1972) have used this principle to remove molybdenum from waters from the Questa molybdenum mine and mill in New Mexico. It is interesting to note that molybdenum is also the chief heavy metal dissolved in waste waters from the mills associated with porphyry copper mines of the southwestern United States. Figure 2 shows that we have been able to remove up to 98 percent of the molybdenum dissolved in waters from copper mills by adding dissolved ferric chloride to the waste waters. The addition of the dissolved ferric iron causes hydrolysis and precipitation of a flocculent precipitate of ferric hydroxide, with a concomitant drop in pH to about 3.5. Maximum removal for the three mill waters investigated (Fig. 2) occurred when the ratio of added iron to dissolved molybdenum was in excess at about ten to one, with the pH allowed to achieve its own final value of about 3.2 to 3.5. We have found similar results by adding large amounts of dissolved aluminum to form aluminum hydroxide, but we have not been able to form precipitates of manganese hydroxide at the necessary low pH with any reasonable quantity of added manganese.

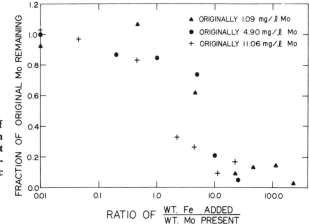

Figure 2. Removal of dissolved molybdenum from aqueous effluent from copper mills by adding dissolved ferric chloride.

COMPARATIVE STUDIES IN COLORADO

One of our principal interests has been to establish some natural datum or baseline of values for molybdenum in waters, soils, sediments, and plants adjacent to an undisturbed molybdenum deposit in an alpine environment. We have hoped to be able to use such an undisturbed, mineralized area to assess the impact of man's activities when a similar deposit is developed and opened for mining and milling, as has occurred at Climax and Urad. Because the Climax mine is an underground operation, we initially thought that we could sample the surficial materials above the deposit as a guide to the concentrations of molybdenum that were present prior to the initiation of mining. Unfortunately, caving and collapse of the surface above the Climax ore bodies has been extensive, thus eliminating the possibility of using this site. As a possible substitute site, we were given permission to study an undeveloped molybdenum deposit on Mount Aetna in the mountains of south-central Colorado (Fig. 1). The altitude, assemblage of molybdenum minerals, type of wallrock, and general alpine environment at Mount Aetna are similar to those at Climax. The area of exposed molybdenum mineralization is much smaller at Mount Aetna than at Climax, but ore-grade samples of molybdenite and ferrimolybdite can be picked up from the outcrop of mineralized bedrock. The mining company that controls most of the deposit on Mount Aetna provided background material to us, in the form of reports and maps. A difference that we did not initially recognize between the areas at Mount Aetna and Climax, however, is the extent of glaciation. The glacial cirque at Climax opens to the west-northwest, whereas the cirque at Mount Aetna opens to the south. This difference in direction of exposure has apparently caused great differences in the extent of glacial erosion in the two areas. Wallace and others (1968, p. 637) stated that most of one entire ore body has been stripped away by streams and glaciers at Climax, with attendant deposition of morainal material that contains abundant fragments of mineralized rock. Although some glaciation has occurred at Mount Aetna, the south-facing slopes have apparently reduced its extent considerably below that of the areas at a similar elevation at Climax. This reduced degree of glaciation, combined with the smaller exposed area of mineralization, makes comparison with Climax extremely tenuous, particularly with regard to the concentration of molybdenum in the soils and sediments of the area.

At Mount Aetna we established a rectilinear grid system around the mineralized exposures of bedrock, with north-south and east-west lines 15 m apart. Using the coordinate system as a guide, we sampled the soils, plants, and bedrock on 30-m centers wherever materials were available. Figure 3 shows the concentration of total molybdenum in the A horizon (upper 5 cm) of the soil. The zone of exposed mineralization is well defined by the concentrations of molybdenum in the soils. Figure 4 shows that similar results are found for the B horizon (at a depth of about 15 cm). There is no apparent concentration of molybdenum in the organic-rich upper layer of this young alpine soil. The soil is at least 1.2 m thick (as determined from trenches) adjacent to the deposit. It is clear that this deposit could have been discovered by geochemical prospecting, using the soil as a guide. We are seeking correlations between the concentrations of molybdenum in the soils and the plants collected from the same grid points. The slurry pH of the soils averaged about 5.5 on Mount Aetna. In these acidic soils, the molybdenum seems to be immobile and relatively unavailable to the plants, and this may also be the reason that we do not see an accumulation of molybdenum in the organic litter on the surface of the soil.

From Figures 3 and 4 it is clear that the concentration of molybdenum in soils adjacent to mineralized bedrock can attain levels of at least hundreds of parts per million in the alpine environment. Such material, if transported down-slope, could significantly increase the concentration of molybdenum in adjacent stream sediments.

Thirteen samples of sediments collected from the small stream that drains the cirque at Mount Aetna show an average of 20 ppm molybdenum. This is in sharp contrast to an average of about 580 ppm molybdenum in ten samples of sediment from the stream below the Climax mine. Because of the difference in extent of erosion and exposure, however, we cannot say that this large difference reflects the mining activities. It is possible that such differences could simply reflect the greater extent of natural transport and deposition of mineralized bedrock at Climax.

Three samples of stream water from Mount Aetna contain an average of 1.2 ppb dissolved molybdenum, compared to hundreds to thousands of parts per billion in the streams below the Climax and Urad mines. Again we face the question of how much of this difference is natural and how much is due to mining and milling. Our waters from Mount Aetna may not have had an opportunity to equilibrate with the molybdenum-rich bedrock and soils of the area. On the other hand, increased mining and milling activites at Urad (Fig. 1) are probably indicated by changes in the concentration of molybdenum in Clear Creek. In October 1963 and December 1965, samples of water from Clear Creek near Golden contained 2 and 1 ppb molybdenum, respectively (Voegeli and King, 1969, Table 1), compared to concentrations from about 120 to 580 ppb for 25 samples collected from mid-August through November 1971 (Jorden, 1971, Fig. 8).

Barakso and Bradshaw (1971) showed by means of leaching experiments that as much as 250 ppm molybdenum could go into solution at high pH from oxide-rich molybdenum ores, although they state that their experimental apparatus did not allow them to simulate natural conditions. A meaningful comparison can also be drawn to the work of Brundin and Nairis (1972) in northern Sweden. In a study of 1,057 samples of water from an area with scattered molybdenum mineralization, they found that 28 ppb represents the 95th percentile of values. The average pH of the waters sampled by Brundin and Nairis was 6.47, compared to 6.3 for 13 samples from our study at Mount Aetna.

In order to get around the difficulty inherent in trying to compare two areas, we have initiated two additional lines of study: (1) In order to obtain an estimate of the concentration of molybdenum in the soils and sediments of the Climax area, we intend to sample the glacial debris that has been spread down the valleys below the mine. (2) We have constructed an experimental apparatus in which we can leach various solid materials while controlling the Eh and pH to simulate natural conditions. From these experiments we hope to be able to predict what concentrations of molybdenum might be expected in various waters in contact with molybdenum ores, soils, minerals, and mill tailings.

CONCENTRATIONS OF MOLYBDENUM
BELOW CLIMAX MILL

We discovered some interesting trends in the concentration of molybdenum in various materials below the mine and mill at Climax (Fig. 5). Tenmile Creek drains the deposit at Climax, whereas the Blue River to the east drains a relatively nonmineralized mountain valley. The sediments in Tenmile Creek above Dillon Reservoir contain an average of 260 ppm Mo (seven samples), whereas the sediments in the Blue River to the east contain 4 ppm Mo (four samples, Fig. 5). Sediments in the Blue River below Dillon and Green Mountain Reservoirs show an intermediate concentration of molybdenum of 39 ppm. Soils below Climax are also enriched in molybdenum relative to those along the Blue River above Dillon Reservoir. The concentration of molybdenum in the water of the Blue River above Dillon Reservoir ranges from near 0 to 9 ppb (four samples), compared to hundreds

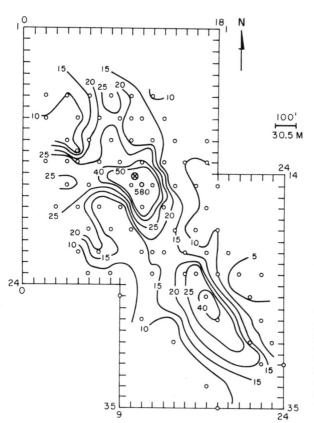

Figure 3. Distribution of total molybdenum (ppm dry weight) in A horizon of soils from Mount Aetna, Colorado, summer 1971. Circled X shows center of exposed mineralization in bedrock.

of parts per billion in Tenmile Creek below Climax. Intermediate concentrations of molybdenum (150 to 400 ppb, nine samples) are also found in the Blue River below Dillon Reservoir. Of the many types of plants that we sampled, only willow seems to show a consistent relation to the concentration of molybdenum in the adjacent environment. The concentration of molybdenum in nine samples of willow below Climax ranges from 12 to 28 ppm by dry weight (Fig. 5), compared to 0.1 to 1.1 ppm Mo in willows from the nonmineralized Blue River. Below Dillon Reservoir, 17 samples of willow show intermediate values from 0.9 to 6 ppm molybdenum.

ANALYTICAL METHODS

The chemical analyses reported in the above sections were obtained by two different techniques, wet chemical analysis and x-ray fluorescence. A detailed description of these methods is available in the References Cited or from us. The x-ray fluorescence technique is currently under development in our laboratories.

Soil, sediment, and pulverized rock samples were dried for 12 hr in an oven

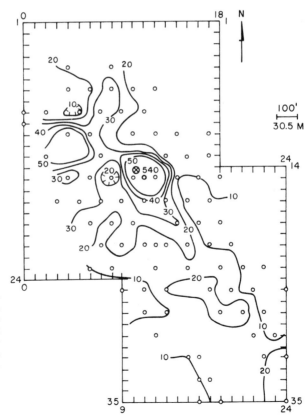

Figure 4. Distribution of total molybdenum (ppm dry weight) in B horizon of soils from Mount Aetna, Colorado, summer 1971. Circled X shows center of exposed mineralization in bedrock.

at 70° C. The samples were then sieved through an 80-mesh, stainless-steel sieve. The fraction passing through the sieve was again dried in an oven at 70° C for 12 hr. All of the chemical analyses reported were performed on this fraction.

A portion of the dry, sieved soil was mixed with reagent-grade potassium pyrosulfate ($K_2S_2O_7$) and fused in a Pyrex test tube (Barakso, 1967). The fusions were dissolved in 1.0 N hydrochloric acid and were filtered and analyzed by the conventional spectrophotometric-thiocyanate method (Ward, 1951). This procedure permits quick analysis of a large number of samples. The method is capable of detecting the Mo in soils above 2 ppm with a relative analytical error of about 10 percent. (The precision can be improved with some procedural modifications.)

All plant samples were dried for 24 hr in an oven at 70°C. The dry plants were then ashed in Pyrex beakers at 450°C to a constant weight (48 to 72 hr is sufficient for most plants). Tests showed no loss of molybdenum at this ashing temperature. Portions of the plants were homogenized and analyzed both by the thiocyanate procedure and by x-ray fluorescence. Because of the greater length of time required, the wet chemical analyses were performed on splits of 20 percent of the samples analyzed by x-ray fluorescence. Agreement between the two methods

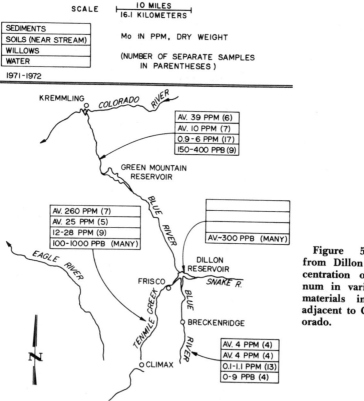

Figure 5. Samples from Dillon area. Concentration of molybdenum in various natural materials in drainages adjacent to Climax, Colorado.

of analysis is about ±10 percent for plant ashes containing more than 10 ppm Mo.

Water samples were generally analyzed by the thiocyanate method. Two different modifications of this procedure have been used; a screening or semiquantitative method and a quantitative method. The semiquantitative method has precision limits of ±15 ppb. The quantitative method, without prior concentration of the sample, can provide results with an absolute precision of a few parts per billion. Water samples that were found to be below the easily accessible concentration range of the thiocyanate method were concentrated by evaporation.

We have also used atomic absorption analysis, but the lack of sensitivity of this method for molybdenum often precludes it as a routine technique in our work.

SUMMARY

Molybdenum is a heavy metal that is being released into the environment in anomalously large amounts in Colorado. It is also the chief dissolved metal in the waste waters from mills associated with the large porphyry copper deposits of the southwestern United States. Although molybdenum does not seem to pose an acute hazard to man, it can cause illness in ruminant animals if it is present in concentrations above about 10 ppm in the forage.

The geochemistry of molybdenum is unusual in that it occurs as an anionic species in natural waters. Unlike many other heavy metals, molybdenum is more mobile at high values of pH than at low values. In acid soils it is relatively immobile. Molybdenum can be removed from industrial waste waters by adsorption or coprecipitation on metal hydroxides at low pH.

After mining and milling activities have begun, it is extremely difficult to determine what the original natural concentrations of molybdenum were in the vicinity of an ore deposit. Man's activities disrupt the surface and drainages near the deposit that is being exploited, and geologically similar areas may differ in significant details.

ACKNOWLEDGMENT

This work was funded under Contract No. GI–34814X from the Rann Division of the National Science Foundation.

REFERENCES CITED

Barakso, J. J., 1967, Geochemical field kit for the determination of trace amounts of molybdenum: Econ. Geology, v. 62, p. 732–738.

Barakso, J. J., and Bradshaw, B. A., 1971, Molybdenum surface depletion and leaching, in Boyle, R. W., ed., Geochemical exploration, Proc. 3rd Internat. Geochem. Explor. Symp., Toronto, April 11–18, 1970: Canadian Inst. Mining and Metallurgy, Spec. Vol. 11, p. 78–84.

Bhappu, R. B., Reynolds, D. H., and Roman, R. J., 1965, Molybdenum recovery from sulfide and oxide ores: Jour. Metals, November, p. 1199–1205.

Brundin, N. H., and Nairis, B., 1972, Alternative sample types in regional geochemical prospecting: Jour. Geochem. Explor., v. 1, no. 1, p. 7–46.

Christianson, G. A., 1970, Report on molybdenosis in farm animals and its relationship to a uraniferous lignite ashing plant: North Dakota Dept. Health (informal rept.), 9 p.

Clark, K. F., 1972, Stockwork molybdenum deposits in the western Cordillera of North America: Econ. Geology, v. 67, no. 6, p. 731–758.

Cohen, H. J., Frodovich, I., and Rajagopalan, K. V., 1971, Hepatic sulfite oxidase: Jour. Biol. Chem., v. 246, no. 2, p. 347–382.

Federal Water Pollution Control Administration, 1968, Water quality criteria (reprinted 1972): Washington, D.C., U.S. Environmental Protection Agency, 234 p.

Hansuld, J. A., 1966, Behavior of molybdenum in secondary dispersion media: Mining Eng., December, p. 73–78.

Hem, J. D., 1970, Study and interpretation of the chemical characteristics of natural water (2d ed.): U.S. Geol. Survey Water-Supply Paper 1473, 363 p.

Jones, L.H.P., 1957, The solubility of molybdenum in simplified systems and aqueous soil suspensions: Jour. Soil Sci., v. 8, no. 2, p. 311–327.

Jorden, R. M., 1971, Environmental reconnaissance of sources and routes of transport of molybdenum, in An interdisciplinary study of transport and biological effects of molybdenum in the environment: An interim progress report submitted to the National Science Foundation by The Molybdenum Project: Boulder, Univ. Colorado, p. 13–41.

Kopp, J. F., and Kroner, R. C., 1967, Trace metals in waters of the United States: Cincinnati, Ohio, U.S. Dept. Interior, Federal Water Pollution Control Admin., 208 p.

Kubota, J., Lazar, V. A., Langan, L. N., and Beeson, K. C., 1961, The relationship of soils to molybdenum toxicity in cattle in Nevada: Soil Sci. Soc. America Proc., v. 25, p. 227–232.

Kubota, J., Lemon, E. R., and Allaway, W. H., 1963, The effect of soil moisture content upon the uptake of molybdenum, copper, and cobalt by alsike clover: Soil Sci. Soc. America Proc., v. 27, no. 6, p. 679–683.

Pérez, E. A., 1972, Toxicity and removal of molybdenum from wastewaters: Albuquerque, N.M., Spec. Rept. to Dept. Civil Engineering, 60 p.

Sauchelli, V., 1969, Trace elements in agriculture: New York, Van Nostrand Reinhold Co., p. 133–149.

Titley, S. R., and Anthony, J. W., 1961, Some preliminary observations on the theoretical geochemistry of molybdenum under supergene conditions: Arizona Geol. Soc. Digest, v. IV, p. 103–116.

Underwood, E. J., 1971, Trace elements in human and animal nutrition: New York, Academic Press, 543 p.

Voegeli, P. T., and King, R. U., 1969, Occurrence and distribution of molybdenum in surface water of Colorado: U.S. Geol. Survey Water-Supply Paper 1535-N, 32 p.

Wallace, S. R., Muncaster, N. K., Jonson, D. C., MacKenzie, W. B., Bookstrom, A. A., and Surface, V. E., 1968, Multiple intrusion and mineralization at Climax, Colorado, in Ridge, J. D., ed., Ore deposits of the United States, 1933–1967: New York, Am. Inst. Mining, Metall., and Petroleum Engineers, p. 605–640.

Ward, F. N., 1951, Determination of molybdenum in soils and rocks: Anal. Chemistry, v. 23, p. 788–791.

PAPER PRESENTED AT THE 1972 ANNUAL MEETING OF THE GEOLOGICAL SOCIETY OF AMERICA IN MINNEAPOLIS, MINNESOTA

MANUSCRIPT RECEIVED BY THE SOCIETY SEPTEMBER 17, 1973

REVISED MANUSCRIPT RECEIVED SEPTEMBER 23, 1974

Geological Society of America
Special Paper 155
© 1975

Cadmium-Zinc Interactions: Implications for Health

HAROLD H. SANDSTEAD

AND

LESLIE M. KLEVAY
USDA Human Nutrition Laboratory
P.O. Box D, University Station
Grand Forks, North Dakota 58201

INTRODUCTION

Cadmium and zinc are chemically similar (Cotzias and others, 1961; Cotton and Wilkinson, 1966). They therefore compete with one another for a variety of ligands (Pulido and others, 1966a; Gunn and others, 1968). Because cadmium is considered to have only adverse effects in biological systems (Friberg and others, 1971) and zinc is an essential nutrient (Sandstead, 1973), the significance of their competitive interactions for health merits investigation.

In this paper we will examine the hypothesis that competition between zinc and cadmium for biological ligands has important implications for health.

ZINC AND CADMIUM IN THE ENVIRONMENT

Cadmium is a relatively rare element. Its average concentration in the Earth's crust is about 0.5 ppm (Heindl, 1970). In nature it is closely associated with zinc (Friberg and others, 1971). The zinc:cadmium ratio of most minerals and soils ranges from 100:1 to 12,000:1 (Bowen, 1966; Schroeder and others, 1967).

In the United States, cadmium is obtained commercially only as a by-product during the processing of zinc-bearing ores (Heindl, 1970). Its production has risen steadily during the past three decades (Moulds, 1969). This growth can be described by the equation $y = 0.21x - 1.81$, where y represents the annual production in millions of pounds and x is the year minus 1900.

Sixty percent (8 million pounds in 1968) of the cadmium produced each year is used for electroplating (Heindl, 1970), and products plated with cadmium are widely used throughout the United States (Flick and others, 1971). Such cadmium-plated products and cadmium-containing materials may be hazardous to man in certain situations. Examples of such situations include the cutting of cadmium-plated bolts with a torch (Zavon and Meadows, 1970) or the use of cadmium-containing silver solder in a poorly ventilated space (Winston, 1971). Inappropriate use of cadmium-plated refrigerator shelves for grilling food has also resulted in poisoning by ingestion (Baker and Hafner, 1961).

Thirteen percent (Heindl, 1970) of the annual production of cadmium is used in pigments incorporated into plastics, paints, enamels, lacquers, and printing ink. The manufacture of batteries accounts for 3 percent. Cadmium also enters the environment through its presence in the fumes of lead and copper smelters.

Cadmium salts of stearic acid are used (2.5 million pounds in 1968) as stabilizers (Heindl, 1970) in thermoplastics, such as polyvinylchloride, a material widely used in the packaging of food. Whether the cadmium in such plastics can migrate into foods is apparently unknown. It is known, however, that phthalate esters have leached into human blood from the polyvinylchloride bags in which it was stored (Jaeger and Rubin, 1972). The use of cadmium in plastics may have decreased since the introduction of dioctyl tin stabilizers (Wood, 1968).

Plastic (polyvinylchloride) pipes are being used increasingly. To our knowledge, reliable data regarding the extraction of cadmium from such pipes by water have not been published. On the other hand, it is well known that cadmium in solder and galvanizing dissolves in soft water passing through water pipes. The consequences of such a phenomenon have been illustrated by the finding of 8.3 ppm cadmium in running water from the cold water tap and 15 to 77 ppm in cold water that had been stagnant in the pipes of a municipal hospital. Hot water contained 21 ppm (Schroeder and others, 1967).

The close association of cadmium and zinc is also important in agriculture. Because it is difficult to remove cadmium from zinc, the zinc sulfate used to manufacture super phosphate fertilizers contains 15 to 21 ppm cadmium (Hammer and others, 1971). The fertilizer itself may contain 2 to 20 ppm cadmium. Use of superphosphate fertilizers releases 50,000 to 500,000 lb of cadmium into the environment each year (USDA and TVA, 1964). Another potential source of cadmium in food is sewer sludge, a material rich in nitrogen phosphate, macro-elements, trace metals, and toxic heavy metals (Larson and others, 1972). Cadmium concentrations of sludge from various sources have been found to range from 6 to 369 ppm. Sources of the sludge appear to be responsible for these wide differences. When the amount of industrial wastes is high, the cadmium content is increased. The entry of this cadmium into plants is a subject of current investigation.

ENTRY OF CADMIUM INTO MAN

Cadmium enters man from several sources (Table 1). These include air, cigarette smoke, drinking water, and food. The contributions of these various sources to the body burden of cadmium are dependent on the amount of cadmium in the source material, the physiochemical characteristics of the source material that affect solubility of the cadmium, and factors in the body, which affect solubility of cadmium and its movement across the intestinal mucosa and through the

TABLE 1. ENVIRONMENTAL LEVELS: USUAL INTAKE AND RETENTION OF CADMIUM

Range	Usual intake/day (μg)
Air 0.01 to 0.2 μg/m^3	0.5
Cigarette smoke 0.7 to 0.8 μg/whole cigarette	3.0
Drinking water 0 to 30 μg/l	5.0
Food 30 to 200 μg/day	50
Usual total intake/day	58.5
Nonurban, nonsmoking, low-cadmium foods	32
Urban, smoking (3 pk), high-cadmium foods	190

Retention		
Inhalation	10 to 40%; 3.5 μg × 0.25 = 0.875	μg
Ingestion	3 to 8%; 55.0 μg × 0.05 = 2.750	μg
Total	3.625	μg
Excretion (of that absorbed)	Stool 10%; 3.625 = 0.360	μg
	Urine = 1.500	μg
Total	1.860	μg
Net daily retention	1.765	μg
Net 50-yr retention	32.3	mg
Net 50-yr renal cortical Cd	50	μg/g of tissue

body. Thus the factors that influence the total body burden of cadmium are complex. Because food and water are the major sources of cadmium, those factors that influence the availability of cadmium for intestinal absorption are the most important.

The usual daily intake of cadmium by urban man has been estimated (Friberg and others, 1971). The amounts of cadmium in air, cigarette smoke, drinking water, and food are shown in Table 1. From these data one can estimate the probable daily absorption, excretion, and retention of cadmium. Thus an urban adult could retain 1.77 μg of cadmium daily, an amount sufficient to result in a retention of 32 mg of cadmium in 50 yr. The renal cortex of such an individual would contain approximately 50 ppm, an amount in the range found by Tipton on analysis of renal tissue from urban men (Schroeder and others, 1967). It has been suggested by Friberg that a renal cortical concentration of approximately 200 ppm is necessary before gross pathological effects (proteinurea) occur. This level of renal cadmium correlates with a body burden of 120 mg. To accumulate 120 mg of cadmium in 50 yr, a dietary intake of approximately 160 μg daily would be necessary if the intake from the other sources listed in Table 1 were similar. This level of intake probably does occur in some heavy-smoking urban individuals who consume foods rich in cadmium (Schroeder and Balassa, 1961).

RELATIONSHIP OF DIETARY
ZINC AND DIETARY CADMIUM

Man obtains most of his zinc from his diet. As noted above, this is also true for cadmium. The amount of zinc in the diet may vary widely depending on the diet composition. Some diets reported in the literature (Sandstead, 1973) contained 5 to 20 mg.

The availability of dietary zinc for absorption is also influenced by the diet composition. The digestability of the food is a crucial factor. Hence zinc in meat, sea food, or milk products (which are readily digested by normal man) is considerably more available than zinc in grains, legumes, and other vegetables, which contain phytate or other ligands that can complex with zinc to form insoluble chelates in the alkaline environment of the small intestine. Presumably, cadmium behaves in a manner similar to zinc in the intestinal milieu. Its low availability for intestinal absorption from food (3 to 8 percent) compared with an approximately 20 to 30 percent availability of zinc (Sandstead, 1973) suggests that, in fact, most of the cadmium present in food is firmly bound to insoluble ligands during the process of digestion, with the result that 95 percent or more of dietary cadmium is excreted in the stool.

Reported zinc (Schroeder and others, 1967) and cadmium (Schroeder and Balassa, 1961) contents of selected foods are listed in Table 2. Though the absolute amounts of these two elements in food are important, their availability from foods is perhaps an even more important factor as far as the toxic effects of food cadmium and the protective effects of zinc are concerned.

Observations on the zinc:cadmium ratio in wheat, whole-wheat flour, and white flour indicate that the distributions of zinc and cadmium within the wheat grain are different. As wheat is refined, the ratio decreases from 120:1 in wheat to 65:1 in whole-wheat flour to 26:1 in white flour (Schroeder and others, 1967). Presumably, a similar relationship is present in other grains. The implication of the difference in distribution of zinc and cadmium in raw grain is that refining decreases the relative amount of the essential nutrient, zinc, while increasing the relative amount of the toxic element, cadmium, in the final food product.

TABLE 2. CONCENTRATIONS OF Zn* AND Cd† IN FOODS (PPM)

	Oyster	Canned tuna	Beef steak	Beef liver	Pork chops
Zn	1487.0	17.4	56.6	39.2	3.6
Cd	0.65	0.06	0.024	0.20	0.025

	Homog. milk	Whole egg	White flour	Corn meal	Lima beans
Zn	0.1–0.5	20.8	8.9	9.0	31.5
Cd	tr	tr	0.059	0.065	0

	Potatoes	Kidney beans	Lettuce
Zn	8.7	0.80	1.6
Cd	0	0.052	0.17

*Data from Schroeder and others (1967).
† Data from Schroeder and Balassa (1961).

ZINC AND CADMIUM INTERACTIONS IN THE BODY

Within the body, zinc and cadmium are primarily complexed with intracellular ligands. Zinc is necessary for the activity of many metalloenzymes and metal-dependent enzymes (Parisi and Vallee, 1969). In addition, zinc is complexed with nucleoproteins and other nonenzyme proteins and influences their tertiary and (or) quaternary structure. In liver, kidney, and intestinal mucosa, zinc is also bound to metallothionine. Metabolically, zinc is essential for the synthesis of nucleic acids (Sandstead and others, 1972; Terhune and Sandstead, 1972) and proteins (Hsu and others, 1969), functions that may explain its role in growth (Sandstead and others, 1967) and tissue repair (Sandstead and others, 1970).

Cadmium, in contrast to zinc, has no known metabolic function. Within cells its only known effects are those of toxicity. Cadmium binds firmly to mercapto groups of proteins and is thus firmly bound to metallothionine, a protein with many free sulfhydryl groups (Pulido and others, 1966b; Kagi and Vallee, 1961). The affinity of cadmium for mercapto groups is many times that of zinc. Thus it may displace zinc from sulfur ligands and may inhibit certain reactions dependent on the presence of zinc.

Equine kidney metallothionine has been found to contain 59,500 ppm cadmium, 16,900 ppm zinc, 310 ppm iron, and 1,500 ppm copper, a total of 8.4 G-atoms of metal per 10,000 mol. wt. The free sulfhydryl groups, due to a large proportion of cysteinyl residues, are 26 per mole. As the function of metallothionine has not been fully clarified and as it appears to protect sensitive enzyme systems within cells by binding with cadmium and other metals, metallothionine may be considered a "scavenger protein" until some other function is identified.

The fact that cadmium binds firmly to sulfhydryl groups has suggested to us that it may react with the enzyme superoxide dismutase. This enzyme has two free sulfhydryl groups (Hartz and Deutsch, 1972) in addition to two atoms of zinc and two of copper (Carrico and Deutsch, 1970) per molecule.

Superoxide dismutase catalyses the reaction $O_2^- + O_2^- + 2H^+ \rightarrow O_2 + H_2O_2$ (McCord and Fridovich, 1969), thus protecting the electron transport system of cells from the accumulation of free radicals (McCord and Fridovich, 1970). It has been postulated that free radicals may damage cells and thus accelerate the aging process (Harman, 1956). In addition, they are thought to contribute to the cellular damage caused by ionizing radiation (Little, 1968).

It seems possible that cadmium may decrease the activity of superoxide dismutase, either by binding its sulfhydryl groups and thus altering the tertiary structure of the molecule, or perhaps by displacing zinc or copper from their sites on the protein. The possible consequences for health of such a reaction by cadmium are obvious, if the free radical theory of aging is true. Metallothionine, through its "scavenger" effect, may tend to protect superoxide dismutase and other susceptible enzymes from the injurious effects of cadmium and excesses of other transition metals. The postulated binding of sulfhydryl groups of superoxide dismutase by cadmium has been shown for several other enzymes (Simon and others, 1947). The adverse effects of cadmium on oxidative phosphorylation (Jacobs and others, 1956) may be explained either by disruption of the transport of electrons (McCord and Fridovich, 1970), if free radicals accumulate secondary to inhibition of superoxide dismutase, or by the binding of the dithiol groups of lipoamide dehydrogenase. This latter enzyme is readily inhibited by lead (Ulmer and Vallee, 1969) and is therefore presumably susceptible to inhibition by cadmium. It is part of the macro-molecular complex of enzymes that synthesize acetyl coenzyme A and succinyl coenzyme A from pyruvate and α-keto glutarate, respectively.

To our knowledge, an in vivo inhibition by cadmium of enzymes activated by zinc has not been shown. Even so, it is probable that cadmium does inhibit certain of the metabolic functions of zinc. The protective effect of zinc—against the toxic effects of cadmium on testes (Gunn and others, 1968), against cadmium induced sarcomas (Gunn and others, 1964), and the reversibility of cadmium-induced hypertension in rats by parenterally administered zinc chelate (Na_2Zn–CDTA) (Schroeder and others, 1968)—supports this thesis.

Under usual circumstances, roughly one-third of the body cadmium is found in the renal cortex. There it is concentrated in the proximal tubular cells of the nephron. High concentrations of cadmium in these cells have adverse effects on their reabsorptive function. In man an extreme manifestation of the toxic effects of cadmium on the renal tubule is iti-iti disease. Patients with this disease come from a region in Japan where the water is contaminated with zinc and cadmium. Thus rice raised in the water contains high levels of these elements. The clinical features of iti-iti include an "adult Fanconi's" syndrome similar to that which has been observed associated with injury to the renal tubules by other toxic metals. Tubular reabsorption of glucose, amino acids, protein, phosphate, and certain electrolytes may be impaired. Osteomalacia, microfractures, bone pain, and crippling deformities occur (Friberg and others, 1971).

Another organ that is adversely affected by cadmium in experimental animals is the arterial wall. Chronic feeding (1 yr) of low concentration (5 ppm) of cadmium will produce hypertension in Long-Evans female rats (Schroeder and others, 1968). It seems probable that the hypertension observed is a consequence of a direct effect of cadmium on the vessel wall, as acutely injected cadmium has been shown to have an immediate vasoconstrictor effect on testicular vessels (Gunn and others, 1968), on the isolated hind limb of the rat (Perry and others, 1967), and on the intra-arterially perfused intact rat (Perry and others, 1970). In addition, cadmium is bound by the tissues of the perfused hind limb and to isolated strips of aorta (Perry and others, 1970). A direct effect of cadmium on the arteries of the renal cortex is inferred by the finding that the plasma renin activity (Perry, 1971) and sodium retention of rats injected with cadmium are increased (Perry and others, 1971). These findings may provide an explanation for the hypertension observed in Long-Evans rats that were fed cadmium chronically.

In man, a causal role for cadmium in the genesis of hypertension is less clear. Perry (1971) has reviewed the evidence for this. He noted that renal concentrations of cadmium vary with the geographic origin of the individual (Perry and others, 1961), and that hypertensive Americans were found by Schroeder (1965) to have higher concentrations of renal cadmium than nonhypertensive Americans; in a later study, Morgan (1969) did not find such a relationship. On a world-wide basis, the incidence of hypertension is greater in those populations in which higher concentrations of renal cadmium occur. More recent epidemiologic studies of individuals exposed industrially to cadmium have not shown a relationship between cadmium and hypertension (Hammer and others, 1971). A similar negative relationship has been found between the intake of cadmium in milk and cardiovascular disease (Pinkerton and others, 1971).

A recent autopsy study (Voors and others, 1975) of individuals from the Piedmont region and coastal plain of North Carolina has revealed a positive correlation between renal cortical cadmium:zinc ratio and the severity of atherosclerosis as judged by examination of the arteries at autopsy. Additionally, it has shown a marginal positive correlation between hypertension as indexed by cardiac weight and the renal cortical cadmium:zinc ratio. This latter relationship appears related either to residence (coastal plain) or race (black). The fact that the coastal plain is a "soft water area" is also of interest in this regard. In Voors and others' (1975) study, a statistical relationship between renal tissue cadmium and atherosclerosis or hypertension was not found. Thus Voors demonstrated the importance of considering the interaction between zinc and cadmium in relation to disease. It seems possible that the failure of epidemiologic studies to find a relationship between cadmium exposure and hypertension or atherosclerosis may have been due to a failure to consider the cadmium:zinc ratio instead of cadmium alone. The experimental findings from animal studies noted above certainly support the hypothesis that cadmium may have adverse cumulative effects on the cardiovascular system.

Additional investigation of the relationships between zinc and cadmium in man is needed. Such research should be done with the recognition that sodium, potassium, lithium, copper, calcium, and magnesium may possibly influence the physiologic effects of the zinc:cadmium interaction. Failure to control these additional variables may result in data that is confusing and may tend to obscure the central issue: the role of cadmium in human disease.

REFERENCES CITED

Baker, T. D., and Hafner, W. G., 1961, Cadmium poisoning from a refrigerator shelf used as an improvised barbecue grill: Pub. Health Rept., v. 76, p. 543–544.

Bowen, H.J.M., 1966, Trace elements in biochemistry: London, Academic Press, 241 p.

Carrico, R. J., and Deutsch, H. F., 1970, The presence of zinc in human cytocuprein and some properties of the apoprotein: Jour. Biol. Chem., v. 245, p. 723–727.

Cotton, F. A., and Wilkinson, G., 1966, Advanced inorganic chemistry: New York, Interscience, p. 600–611.

Cotzias, G. C., Borg, D. C., and Selleck, B., 1961, Virtual absence of turnover in cadmium metabolism: ^{109}Cd studies in the mouse: Am. Jour. Physiol., v. 201, p. 927.

Flick, D. F., Krabill, H. F., and Dimitroff, J. M., 1971, Toxic effects of cadmium: A review: Environmental Research, v. 4, p. 71–85.

Friberg, L., Piscator, M., and Nordberg, G., 1971, Cadmium in the environment: U.S. Dept. Commerce Tech. Rept. APTD–0681, 353 p.

Gunn, S. A., Gould, T. C., and Anderson, W.A.D., 1964, Effect of zinc on carcinogenesis by cadmium: Soc. Exp. Biol. Med. Proc., v. 115, p. 653.

——1968, Mechanisms of zinc, cysteine and selenium protection against cadmium induced vascular injury to mouse testis: Jour. Reprod. Fert., v. 15, p. 65.

Hammer, D. I., Finklea, J. F., Creason, J. P., Sandifer, S. H., Keil, J. E., Priester, L. E., and Stara, J. F., 1971, Cadmium exposure and human health effects, in Hemphill,

D. D., ed., Trace substances in environmental health—V: Columbia, Univ. Missouri, p. 269.

Harman, D., 1956, Aging: A theory based upon free radical and radiation chemistry: Jour. Gerontology, v. 11, p. 298–300.

Hartz, J. W., and Deutsch, H. F., 1972, Subunit structure of human superoxide dismutase: Jour. Biol. Chem., v. 247, p. 7043–7050.

Heindl, R. A., 1970, Cadmium, in Mineral facts and problems: U.S. Dept. Interior, Bur. Mines Bull., no. 650, p. 515–526.

Hsu, J. M., Anthony, W. L., and Buchanan, P. J., 1969, Zinc deficiency and incorporation of 14C-labeled methionine into tissue proteins in rats: Jour. Nutrition, v. 99, p. 425.

Jacobs, E. E., Jacob, M., Sanadi, D. R., and Bradley, L. B., 1956, Uncoupling of oxidative phosphorylation by cadmium ion: Jour. Biol. Chem., v. 223, p. 147.

Jaeger, R. J., and Rubin, R. J., 1972, Migration of a phthalate ester plasticizer from polyvinyl chloride blood bags into stored human blood and its localization in human tissue: New England Jour. Med., v. 287, p. 1114–1118.

Kagi, J.H.R., and Vallee, B. L., 1961, Metallothionine: A cadmium and zinc-containing protein from equine renal cortex: Jour. Biol. Chem., v. 236, p. 2435.

Larson, W. E., Clapp, C. E., and Dowdy, R. H., 1972, Interim report on the agricultural value of sewage sludge: St. Paul, Minn., USDA, ARS and Soil Science Dept., Univ. Minnesota, Metropolitan Sewer Board.

Little, J. B., 1968, Cellular effects of ionizing radiation: New England Jour. Med., v. 278, p. 308-315, 369-376.

McCord, J. M., and Fridovich, I., 1969, Superoxide dismutase. An enzymatic function for erythrocuprein (hemocuprein): Jour. Biol. Chem., v. 244, p. 6049–6055.

——1970, The utility of superoxide dismutase in studying free radical reactions II. The mechanism of the mediation of cytochrome c reduction by a variety of electron carriers: Jour. Biol. Chem., v. 245, p. 1374–1377.

Morgan, J. M., 1969, Tissue cadmium concentrations in man: Arch. Int. Med., v. 123, p. 405.

Moulds, D. E., 1969, Cadmium, in Minerals yearbook-I: U.S. Dept. Interior, U.S. Govt. Printing Office, p. 235–240. (See also articles with the same title in the yearbooks for 1945, 1949, 1953, 1957, 1961, and 1965.)

Parisi, A. F., and Vallee, B. L., 1969, Zinc metalloenzymes: Characteristics and significance in biology and medicine: Am. Jour. Clin. Nutr., v. 22, p. 1222.

Perry, H. M., Jr., 1971, Trace elements related to cardiovascular disease, in Cannon, H. L., and Hopps, H. C., eds., Geochemical environment in health and disease: Boulder, Colorado, Geol. Soc. America Mem. 123, p. 179.

Perry, H. M., Jr., Tipton, I. H., Schroeder, H. A., Steiner, R. L., and Cook, M. J., 1961, Variation in the concentration of cadmium in human kidney as a function of age and geographic origin: Jour. Chron. Dis., v. 14, p. 259.

Perry, H. M., Jr., Erlanger, M., Yunice, A., and Perry, E. F., 1967, Mechanism of acute hypertensive effect of intra-arterial cadmium and mercury in anesthetized rats: Jour. Lab. Clin. Med., v. 70, p. 963.

Perry, H. M., Jr., Erlanger, M., Yunice, A., Schoepfle, E., and Perry, E. F., 1970, Hypertension and tissue metal levels following intravenous cadmium, mercury and zinc: Am. Jour. Physiol., v. 219, p. 755.

Perry, H. M., Jr., Perry, E. F., and Purifoy, J. E., 1971, Antinaturitic effect of intra-muscular cadmium in rats, in Friberg, L., Piscator, M., and Nordberg, G., Cadmium in the environment: U.S. Dept. Commerce Tech. Rept. APTD–0681.

Pinkerton, C., Creason, J. P., Shay, C. M., Hammer, D. I., Buechley, R. W., Murthy,

G. K., 1971, Cadmium content of milk and cardiovascular disease mortality, in Hemphill, D. D., ed., Trace substances in environmental health—V: Columbia, Missouri, Univ. Missouri, p. 285.

Pulido, P., Fuwa, K., and Vallee, B. L., 1966a, A determination of cadmium in biological materials by atomic absorption spectroscopy: Ann. Biochem., v. 14, p. 393.

Pulido, P., Kagi, J.H.R., and Vallee, B. L., 1966b, Isolation and some properties of human metallothionine: Biochem., v. 5, p. 1768.

Sandstead, H. H., 1973, Zinc nutrition in the USA: Am. Jour. Clin. Nutr., v. 26, p. 1251.

Sandstead, H. H., Prasad, A. S., Schulert, A. R., Frarid, Z., Miale, A., Jr., Bassilly, S., and Darby, W. J., 1967, Human zinc deficiency endocrine manifestation and response to treatment: Am. Jour. Clin. Nutr., v. 20, p. 422.

Sandstead, H. H., Lanier, V. C., Shepard, G. H., and Gillespie, D. D., 1970, Zinc and wound healing: Am. Jour. Clin. Nutr., v. 23, p. 514.

Sandstead, H. H., Gillespie, D. D., and Brady, R. N., 1972, Zinc deficiency: Effect on brain of the suckling rat: Pediat. Research, v. 6, p. 119.

Schroeder, H. A., 1965, Cadmium as a factor in hypertension: Jour. Chron. Dis., v. 18, p. 647.

Schroeder, H. A., and Balassa, J. J., 1961, Abnormal trace metals in man: Cadmium: Jour. Chron. Dis., v. 14, p. 236.

Schroeder, H. A., Nason, A. P., Tipton, I. H., and Balassa, J. J., 1967, Essential trace metals in man: zinc. Relation to environmental cadmium: Jour. Chron. Dis., v. 20, p. 179–210.

Schroeder, H. A., Nason, A. P., and Mitchner, M., 1968, Action of a chelate of zinc on trace metals and hypertensive rats: Am. Jour. Physiol., v. 214, p. 796.

Simon, F. P., Potts, A. M., and Gerard, R. W., 1947, Action of cadmium and thiols on tissues and enzymes: Arch. Biochem., v. 12, p. 283.

Terhune, M. W., and Sandstead, H. H., 1972, Decreased RNA polymerase activity in mammalian zinc deficiency: Science, v. 177, p. 68.

Ulmer, D. D., and Vallee, B. L., 1969, Effects of lead on biochemical systems, in Hemphill, D. D., ed., Trace substances in environmental health—II: Columbia, Univ. Missouri, p. 7.

USDA and TVA, 1964, Superphosphate: Its history, chemistry and manufacture.

Voors, A. W., Shuman, M. S., and Gallagher, P. N., 1975, Atherosclerosis and hypertension in relation to some trace elements in tissues: World Rev. Nutrition and Dietetics, v. 20, p. 299.

Winston, R. M., 1971, Cadmium fume poisoning: British Med. Jour., v. 2 (5758), p. 401.

Wood, S., 1968, Vinyl bottles, what now?: Modern Plastics, v. 45 (12), p. 78–82.

Zavon, M. R., and Meadows, C. D., 1970, Vascular sequelae to cadmium fume exposure: Am. Ind. Hyg. Assoc. Jour., v. 31, p. 180–182.

PAPER PRESENTED AT THE 1972 ANNUAL MEETING OF THE GEOLOGICAL SOCIETY OF AMERICA IN MINNEAPOLIS, MINNESOTA
MANUSCRIPT RECEIVED BY THE SOCIETY SEPTEMBER 17, 1973
REVISED MANUSCRIPT RECEIVED SEPTEMBER 29, 1974

Geological Society of America
Special Paper 155
© 1975

Therapies for Environmental Element Deficiencies and Toxic Excesses

William H. Strain
Walter J. Pories
Edward G. Mansour
Arthur Flynn
Department of Surgery
Cleveland Metropolitan General Hospital
Case Western Reserve University School of Medicine
Cleveland, Ohio 44109

ABSTRACT

Therapies for environmental element deficiencies and toxic excesses have been only partially perfected for plants, animals, and man, and require much additional study. Chemical and natural fertilizers are frequently applied irrationally to the soil because of incomplete information on (1) nutrient deficiencies and availabilities from the soil; (2) imbalances caused by chemical fallout; (3) translocation mechanisms from soil to plant; and (4) the effect of runoff on water composition. Range-fed domestic and wild animals seem to present more problems than confinement-fed animals because of the lack of quality control of their rations. Apparently, man reflects environmental deficiencies and toxic excesses more than do animals because of man's longer life, free choice of diet, and poor quality control of food. Leaf and hair analyses provide very useful methods of evaluating regional element imbalances and therapies for these imbalances. Further developments of these therapies will provide more and better food and will serve to correct the large geographical differences in life expectancy in the United States. Any large-scale therapy needs constant re-evaluation and improvement, as is illustrated by current problems with air, water, soil, and foodstuffs.

INTRODUCTION

Element deficiencies and toxic excesses in the environment are being investigated extensively. Much evidence for these imbalances has long been available from geological surveys of the composition of rocks, waters, and soils. More recently, additional evidence has accumulated from surveys conducted primarily to define trace- or mineral-element deficiencies in soils. Currently, there is active interest in toxic levels of heavy metals, not only in soil and water, but also in air (Miller and Berg, 1969). The task of correlating environmental element deficiencies and excesses is enormous because all the elements must be considered, and little is known of the biochemistry of these elements and of their interactions.

Although all elements seem to be essential for life, the amount required of each varies greatly. Elements needed in infinitesimal amounts appear to have narrow concentration ranges between essentiality and toxicity, and these elements are usually associated with toxicity at relatively low levels. Elements required in substantial amounts for biological systems are seldom studied for toxicity, but rather for deficiency and for factors that limit their availability. Maintenance of an ideal balance of the elements is of great importance to agriculture, animal husbandry, and human health. As yet, this ideal balance cannot be defined.

Some therapies have been developed to correct environmental deficiencies and toxic excesses, but many more are needed. Successful patterns have been based on supplying the deficient element or elements, and removal or inhibition of the toxicants. These procedures seem obvious, but actually are frequently very difficult to apply because it is not easy to develop techniques that will constantly supply elements in appropriate concentrations or reduce the levels of toxicants.

Correcting deficiencies and toxic excesses varies greatly with the several biological systems and the nature of the problem. Considerable success has been achieved in adjusting soil deficiencies by means of fertilizers because the inanimate earth can be easily manipulated (Epstein, 1971). Nevertheless, toxic excesses in soil present costly problems that are usually not attacked or not solved. Much success has been achieved with domestic animals through feed additives and fortified salt block, particularly in the nutrition of swine and poultry. Relatively little advance has been made for humans, and only therapies correcting deficiencies of iodine, iron, and fluorine have been developed as satisfactory public-health measures. These approaches must be vastly expanded because the majority of the world's population is not served adequately by the measures that have been developed.

GEOGRAPHY OF DEATH

It has been evident for some time from epidemiological studies that there are distinct geographical differences in the risk of dying, just as there have been geographical differences in the past in the incidence of thyroid disease and of dental caries. This geographical difference appears to be true of all countries studied and of all degenerative diseases, although the pattern varies with the disease. The mortality data for the United States are particularly useful because they have been periodically revised for the major degenerative diseases.

Cancer

The geographical differences in the risk of dying from cancer are illustrated by Figure 1. This is taken from the U.S. Public Health Service report (1963) and shows the death rates for all malignant neoplasms for the total population

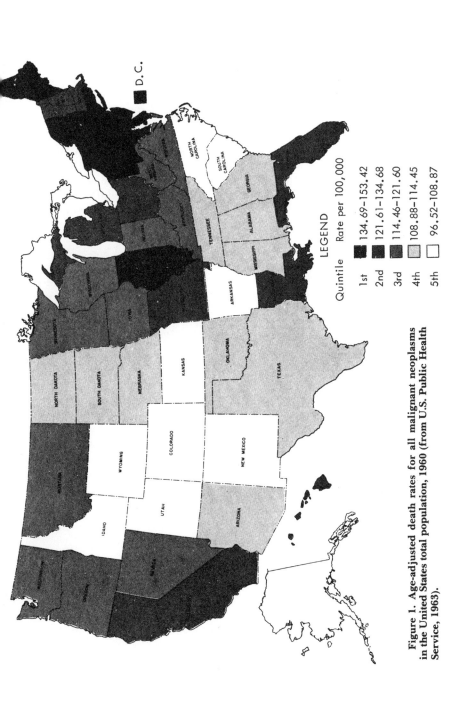

LEGEND

Quintile	Rate per 100,000
1st	134.69–153.42
2nd	121.61–134.68
3rd	114.46–121.60
4th	108.88–114.45
5th	96.52–108.87

Figure 1. Age-adjusted death rates for all malignant neoplasms in the United States total population, 1960 (from U.S. Public Health Service, 1963).

in 1960. In nine of the states, the death rates are extremely low, ranging from 96.52 to 108.87 per hundred thousand, with Utah lowest. In contrast, there are an equal number of states with extremely high death rates, ranging from 134.69 to 153.42 per hundred thousand, with the rate for the District of Columbia the highest. Thus, women in Utah run far less risk of dying from breast cancer than women living in the District of Columbia, and the men in Utah are far less threatened by lung cancer than those in the District.

Many investigations have been conducted on minerals and trace elements in relation to cancer. Most of these studies have been directed toward causal association of one or more elements with cancer. From this work has come the list of so-called carcinogenic metals—arsenic, beryllium, cadmium, chromium, iron, lead, and nickel. In a recent review, Berg and Burbank (1972) discussed these carcinogenic metals in search of correlation between water supplies and cancer mortality, and summarize their conclusions as follows:

No significant correlations were found for iron, cobalt, and chromium. Nickel concentrations correlated with mouth and intestinal cancer death rates, and arsenic concentrations with mortality from larynx cancer, eye cancer, and myeloid leukemia but these cannot be interpreted biologically. Beryllium, which produces bone cancer in animals, was correlated with bone cancer mortality as well as with mortality from breast and uterine cancers, but association was weak in subgroups. Lead, a renal carcinogen in animals and a hematopoietic poison, was correlated with mortality from kidney cancer, leukemias, and lymphomas as well as stomach, intestinal, and ovarian cancers. Cadmium concentrations were correlated most closely and most frequently with cancer death rates, but the distributions of the metal producing these results are not in agreement with other reports.

The conclusion that cadmium concentrations were correlated most closely and most frequently with cancer death rates is supported by some additional evidence. It seems unprofitable, however, to use data on public water supplies when cadmium contamination can occur so easily from solders and plastic connectors in tap water.

Cardiovascular Mortality Rates

That the risk of dying from cardiovascular disease similarly has large geographical differences has been brought out well by Sauer (1962). The map given in Figure 2 shows the age-adjusted cardiovascular mortality rates for 116 economic subregions, nonmetropolitan areas only, whites only, ages 45 to 74, 1949–1951. A number of the Great Plains States have very low death rates ranging from 653.7 to 822.3 per hundred thousand. In contrast, certain states bordering the Atlantic and Pacific Oceans and the Great Lakes have mortality rates ranging from 974.6 to 1358.4 per hundred thousand, or more than double in the extreme instances.

In this analysis, the effect of urban life is eliminated in part by considering nonmetropolitan mortality rates only. A city with a high degree of air pollution must of necessity be surrounded by a "rain shadow" with considerable chemical fallout from low-lying pollution. Thus, the rural water-shed and milk-shed of a metropolitan area can easily be adversely affected by the accumulation of toxic substances in the agricultural area that serves the city with milk, vegetables, and water.

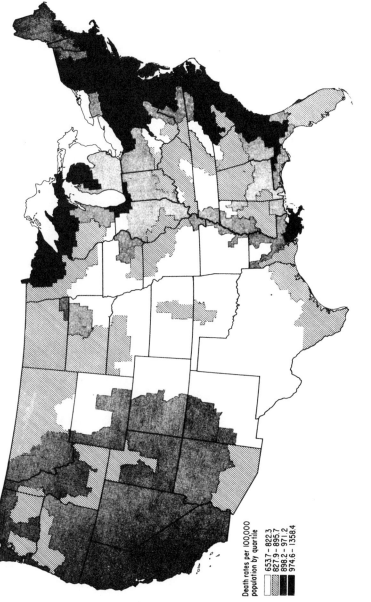

Death rates per 100,000
population by quartile

	653.7 – 822.3
	827.9 – 895.7
	898.2 – 971.2
	974.6 – 1358.4

Figure 2. Age-adjusted cardiovascular mortality rates for 116 economic subregions, nonmetropolitan areas only, whites only, ages 45 to 74, 1949–1951. Age- and sex-adjusted in 10-yr intervals. Excludes population and deaths in metropolitan counties (from Sauer, 1962, with permission).

SOILS

Despite the vast experience accumulated on natural and chemical fertilizers, they are frequently applied irrationally. There is great need for precise methods of soil analysis and of studying the effects of the fertilizer in correcting deficiencies and excesses. Through such measures, both yield and food quality may be expected to increase.

Chemical fertilizers are applied to the soil primarily to supply calcium, nitrogen, phosphorus, and potassium. Only within recent years has interest developed in fuller recognition of the effects of over-application and trace-element deficiencies, particularly of boron, copper, iron, manganese, molybdenum, and zinc. These irrational applications of fertilizer to the soil have been made because of incomplete information on (1) nutrient deficiencies and availabilities; (2) imbalances caused by chemical fallout; (3) translocation mechanisms from soil to plant; and (4) the effects of runoff on water composition.

The nutrient deficiencies and availabilities from the soil can be studied by analyzing leaves collected from plants. As an illustration, the results of Prince (1957) compare the delivering capacity of 10 New Jersey soils in furnishing vanadium and zinc to corn leaves. The data obtained by spectrographic analysis are collected in Table 1. It is evident that the uptake of the two elements in the leaves varies greatly with the type of soil and is very much lower for vanadium than for zinc.

Ecological imbalances caused by chemical fallout hardly need discussion. Lead and mercury problems have attracted the greatest amount of attention, but neither problem is new because contamination from these elements goes back to ancient civilizations. Recognition that organic alkyl mercury derivatives are far more toxic than inorganic compounds is the main thrust of recent work. It may be recalled, however, that Charles II of England, one of the first royal patrons of science, died of overdose of mercury as shown by hair analysis (Lenihan, 1967). Excessive chemical fallout of cadmium and manganese are being studied now, and it is

TABLE 1. VANADIUM- AND ZINC-DELIVERING CAPACITIES OF
TEN NEW JERSEY SOILS*

Loam type	Vanadium		Zinc	
	Soil	Corn leaves	Soil	Corn leaves
	(ppm)		(ppm)	
Norton	119	1.1	180	50
Annandale	90	0.83	108	50
Washington	65	0.37	71	60
Cossayuna	62	0.42	136	17
Croton	50	0.66	60	30
Coltz	46	0.66	68	16
Squires	40	0.40	87	22
Sassafras	33	0.49	63	28
Lansdale	20	0.70	35	66
Collington	11	0.76	21	29
Average	54	0.64	83	37

*From Prince (1957).

reasonable to expect that hair analysis again will demonstrate widespread contamination of the biosphere by these two metals.

The translocation mechanisms from soil to plant are sorely in need of investigation. The organic compounds that participate in these translocations are poorly defined, and membrane permeability is hardly understood at all, even for water-soluble ions like potassium. It is generally recognized that minerals accumulate in the root more than in the aerial parts of the plant, so much so that frequently the ash of the root approaches the soil in composition. Nevertheless, the mineral content of the edible portions of plants varies tremendously (Anonymous, 1971), as does the availability of the minerals. This latter seems to be dependent on complex organic compounds in vegetation. Phytic acid, inositol hexaphosphate, has been studied enough to know that it complexes with iron and zinc to form insoluble calcium ions and thus produces deficiencies. But there are probably many other organic compounds in plants with similar complexing characteristics.

Investigation of the effects of agricultural runoff on water composition has received new impetus. Recent publications on nitrate content of water (Kohl and others, 1971) have emphasized that runoff from fertilizers accumulates in water and that frequently these waters are consumed by man and animals. Reduction of the nitrate to nitrite in the alimentary tract can lead to formation of methemoglobin with fatal outcome. The reported fatalities have been associated with farm animals rather than humans (Fassett, 1966).

DOMESTIC ANIMALS

Therapies for element deficiencies in food animals have been developed extensively since World War I. Currently, there is a good understanding of the mineral requirements of most food animals for calcium, cobalt, copper, fluorine, iodine, iron, magnesium, manganese, molybdenum, phosphorus, salt, selenium, sulfur, and zinc. The Committee on Animal Nutrition, National Research Council, reported on the nutrient requirements of these elements for beef cattle (1970), dairy cattle (1971a), poultry (1971b), sheep (1968a), and swine (1968b). There are also many excellent monographs for each animal species, such as Scott and others (1969) for poultry. These monographs not only discuss the nutritional needs and biochemistry but also give the history of methods of providing adequate animal nutrition.

The progress made in the nutrition of food animals through trace-element preventive therapy has been summarized in many excellent monographs. Underwood (1972) and Hennig (1972) provide overall surveys of trace-element nutrition and soil deficiencies. Current developments are summarized at the annual meetings of the Federation of American Societies for Biological Sciences (FASEB) and at the International Conferences on Trace Elements (Mills, 1970). In addition, there is great interest in trace-element therapies in the USSR, but this literature is not readily accessible.

Salt blocks, fortified first with iodides, and later with many elements, were introduced shortly after World War I. This was one of the first methods used for trace-element therapy and is still widely employed, even though there are serious disadvantages to the block method. Some salts tend to diffuse with moisture so that variable concentrations develop in the block, or almost complete leaching occurs. Potassium iodide, in particular, has presented real problems and is now being replaced by calcium iodate, which is sparingly soluble. The history of providing adequate iodine nutrition for animals in salt blocks has been summarized by Miller and others (1967).

The problem of providing adequate cobalt and selenium for cattle and sheep grazing on forage grown on land deficient in these two elements has been solved by an ingenious method in Australia and New Zealand. Because most of the animals graze on unconfined pastures, fritted clay pellets containing cobalt and (or) selenium in adequate concentrations are administered orally at branding and shearing times. These so-called bullets slowly disintegrate in the alimentary tract and prevent the enormous number of animal fatalities that formerly occurred in these areas.

Range-fed food animals and wild animals are poorly protected against the developments of deficiencies. Recent work by Anke and Groppel (1970) and by Flynn and Franzmann (unpub. data) has shown that magnesium and manganese deficiencies are associated with high mortality in young beef and dairy calves and in young moose calves.

The development of confinement feeding for food animals since World War II holds great promise for complete element therapy. Confined animals do not waste energy in searching for rations, and the feed can be monitored to give high feed efficiency. Recycling of manure to form part of the ration offers an additional method of increasing feed efficiency. Feather and hair analysis provide methods of monitoring nutritional status of animals since inexpensive procedures for most elements have been, or are being, perfected. Thus, confinement feeding offers the possibility not only of reduced meat cost, as exemplified by poultry but also of improving human nutrition through the provision of better-quality protein.

MAN

Man presents many more problems than do soil and domestic animals in applying corrective element therapy. It is impossible to estimate and control the many variations in genetic background, residence, nutrition, use of tobacco, alcohol and drugs, and the effects of industrial and environmental hazards. In addition the longer life span of humans makes it difficult to extrapolate information that can be gained from experimental animals with short life spans. Acute investigations carried out with young experimental animals usually provide little useful information for the resolution of long-term problems in debilitated humans.

Great advances were made in the 20th century in developing therapies for the prevention and treatment of iodine, iron, and fluorine deficiencies in man These developments have taken place mainly in the United States and other technically advanced nations, and much less in the developing countries, where most of the world's people live. The advances are only a beginning because many more elements must be studied and a greater understanding of biological problems and interrelationship must be developed, both for deficiency and toxic excesses.

The public-health measures that supply adequate iodine through iodized salt, iron through ferrous sulfate and other iron medicaments, and fluorine through fluoridated water, have been in operation for more than 25 years. It is evident that there are serious shortcomings associated with each type of therapy. Iodine therapy suffers from the disadvantage that there is little confirmed public emphasis on the use of iodized salt and on avoiding the substances that offset the effectiveness of iodine; consequently, thyroid disease is still a problem, although greatly reduced. Iron lack is widespread in the United States, and more than 25 percent of the population suffers from iron deficiency anemia (Anonymous, 1971). The knowledge that has been accumulated on iron lack and on red cells (Harris and Kellermeyer, 1970) must be greatly extended to encompass the new information on the many variations on the amino acid chain of the globin portion of hemoglobin. Some insight into the enormity of this problem is evident from the tabulation of these many variations by Lehmann and Huntsman (1972). Water with a fluoride content of 1 ppm reduces dental caries by only 50 percent and, obviously, there is much more to be learned about dental caries. The direction of future developments is indicated by recent symposia sponsored by the Geological Society of America (Cannon and Hopps, 1971) and by the United States Department of Agriculture (Mertz and Cornatzer, 1971). Both symposia emphasized the need for more research and knowledge on how to correct deficiencies and toxic excesses, particularly of the trace elements, throughout the food chain and biosphere.

Human exposure to toxic concentrations of elements presents a variety of problems. Elimination of sources of exposure toxicity and provision of lifesaving therapy is usually only the beginning of the treatment. Complete rehabilitation is a long process for which there is very inadequate provision. That many subclinical poisonings from heavy metals, such as lead and mercury, may exist in the general population is a possibility that has barely been explored. Some of the aspects of mercury toxicity problems have been summarized by Miller and Clarkson (1972). Metallic mercury may be essentially free of toxicity in amounts to which the population is usually exposed. Soluble inorganic mercurials can produce severe kidney damage, and organic alkyl mercury compounds have a profound and lasting toxicity on the central nervous system.

IODINE

Iodine is unique among trace elements because it is a constituent of a hormone, thyroxine. Allegedly, the Greeks and Chinese used seaweed and burnt sponges empirically for the treatment of goiter centuries ago. This early experience was not exploited until the 19th century, after the discovery of iodine by Courtois in 1812. Employment of iodine for the treatment of goiter seems to have been made first by Coindet (1820). Epidemiological investigation of the iodine:thyroid concept was delayed, however, until after 1850 when Chatin (1852) made extensive studies on the natural occurrence of iodine in air, water, and soil. Much of Chatin's work was severely questioned at the time, so no action was taken on his suggestion that the water supply in goitrous regions be enriched with iodine.

Toward the end of the 19th century, pathological studies on the thyroid established a much firmer cause-and-effect relationship of iodine deficiency and endemic goiter. Baumann (1896) showed that iodine is a normal constituent of body tissues, and that the iodine content of the thyroid gland, the tissue richest

in iodine, is greatly reduced in endemic goiter. By the end of the century, Baumann'
work had been confirmed and extended by Oswald (1899), who also identified
thyroglobulin.

Thyroxine

Interest next turned to the nature of the active principle of the thyroid gland.
Kendall (1919) isolated a crystalline compound of high activity that he named
thyroxine, which contains 65 percent iodine. It remained for Harington (1926)
to determine the structural formula of thyroxine (II) and for Harington and
Barger (1927) to synthesize the hormone. Thyroxine was considered to be the
only thyroid hormone until 1952 when Gross and Pitt-Rivers (1952) showed that
3,5,3'-triiodothyronine (III) was present in the human thyroid and plasma and
may be as much as three to five times more active as a hormone than thyroxine.
The isolation of triiodothyronine from plasma was forecast when Hird and Trikoju
(1948) detected the compound by paper chromatography from the hydrolysate
of iodocasein. Both hormones are obviously derived from the same parent substance,
thyronine (I).

$$HO-\bigcirc-O-\bigcirc-CH_2-\underset{NH_2}{CH}-COOH$$

I. Thyronine
4-(4'-Hydroxyphenoxy)-Phenylalanine

$$HO-\bigcirc-O-\bigcirc-CH_2-\underset{NH_2}{CH}-COOH$$

II. Thyroxine
3, 5, 3', 5'-Tetraiodothyronine

$$HO-\bigcirc-O-\bigcirc-CH_2-\underset{NH_2}{CH}-COOH$$

III. Liothyronine
3, 5, 3'-Triiodothyronine

Iodized Salt

While these laboratory studies were being carried out on the active principle
of the thyroid gland, effective measures were being developed for the control
of endemic goiter in Switzerland and the United States. In this country, Marine

TABLE 2. GOITER PREVALENCE AMONG SCHOOL CHILDREN IN SELECTED
AREAS, BEFORE AND AFTER INTRODUCTION OF IODIZED SALT*

Area and use of iodized salt	Percent of school children with goiter	
	Before use of iodized salt, 1924	After use of iodized salt, 1936
State of Michigan	38.6	8.2
Regular use of iodized salt	. .	2.9
Non-use of iodized salt	. .	19.3
Cleveland, Ohio	31.0	18.5
Regular use of iodized salt	. .	7.7
Non-use of iodized salt	. .	30.7

*From Kimball (1939) and Pendergrast and others (1961).

and Kimball (1921) furnished much of the leadership for the use of iodized
salt that eventually reduced the incidence of goiter among school children in
Ohio from 32.3 percent in 1925 to 4.0 percent in 1954, and in Michigan from
38.6 percent in 1924 to 1.4 percent in 1951. As shown in Table 2, distinct trends
on the benefits were evident in 1936.

In spite of this progress, there is still much goiter in the United States, and
goiter is still endemic in many parts of the world (World Health Organization,
1960). In the United States, only about 50 percent of the public buys iodized
salt, the method of choice in preventing development of thyroid pathology
(Pendergrast and others, 1961). In other countries, there may be extremes from
none to complete iodization of the salt; in the latter case, there is special provision
for individuals who may have an idiosyncrasy to iodine (Scrimshaw, 1957).

The nature of the problem of determining the level of iodization is well illustrated
by the data of von Fellenburg (1926; Table 3). The iodine content of milk is
probably the best indication of the iodine status of the community, although
all dietary items must be considered. The consumption of goitrogenic substances,
such as members of the cabbage family (Rice, 1938), and of medicinal agents,

TABLE 3. IODINE SOURCES OF GOITER-FREE AND GOITROUS AREAS IN
SWITZERLAND*

	Iodine in quantities of food stated (μg)	
	Chaux-de-Fonds goiter-free	Signau goitrous
Bread, 300 g	4.9	2.4
Potatoes, 500 g	3.5	2.0
Vegetables (mixed), 300 g	4.2	3.1
Milk, butter, and cheese†	13.5	4.5
Apple (or other fruit), 300 g	1.8	0.3
Fat, 60 g	0.6	0.6
Water, 2 l	2.8	0.1
Cooking salt, 10 g	0	0
Total	31.3	13.0

*From von Fellenburg (1926).
†1.5 l (milk equivalent).

such as cobalt and cyanates (Rawson and others, 1943), and derivatives of thiourea (Astwood and others, 1943) must also be studied. This illustrates how complete a survey is necessary in evaluating deficiencies of a trace element.

Potassium iodide is usually the chemical employed for iodization of salt. Recent work indicates that potassium or calcium iodate are superior, particularly where the salt may become damp or be offered in blocks to animals. The level of iodization ranges from 1:10,000 to 1:100,000 (WHO, 1960). Iodine is absorbed very readily from the alimentary tract, but the mechanism of transport and utilization of thyronine through iodination is incompletely understood.

Thyrotoxicosis and Thyroid Cancer

Proper intake of iodine serves to prevent thyrotoxicosis, but it does not seem to inhibit the development of thyroid cancer. This is brought out clearly in the study that Pendergrast and others (1961; Anonymous, 1961a) made contrasting the prevalence rates of simple goiter in males examined for military service during World Wars I and II, and geographic changes in mortality from thyrotoxicosis and thyroid cancer during the same period. The reduction of thyroid disturbance over the 25-year period is shown in Figures 3 and 4. As shown in Figure 5, the reduction in incidence of thyroid disease is much more impressive in the naturally goitrous than in the nongoitrous regions of the United States. These

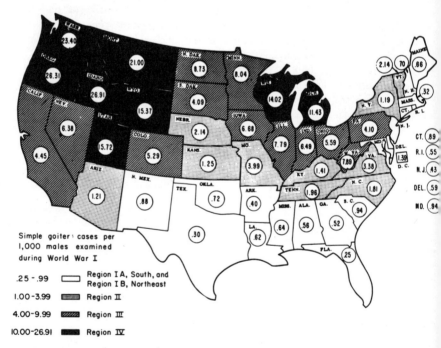

Figure 3. Prevalence rates of simple goiter among males examined for military service during World War I: United States by states, 1917–1918 (from Pendergrast and others, 1961, with permission).

trends and the geographic variations of goiter prevalence may be contrasted with the trends and geographic patterns of mortality attributed to thyrotoxicosis and thyroid cancer represented in Figure 6. The comparisons indicate a highly significant correlation between reduction of goiter and of thyrotoxicosis. In contrast, the data show no evidence of an association between goiter and thyroid cancer.

Toxicity

Iodine has been relatively free of toxic implications other than idiosyncrasy. Although tincture of iodine has been ingested frequently with suicidal intent, it is seldom fatal. Allergic reactions to iodine are itching, skin rashes, and so forth, and are of short duration. Many of these reactions have been recorded as the result of overenthusiastic use of iodides and iodinated organic compounds as contrast media for radiographic diagnoses. The fatalities that have resulted from the contrast media are so well identified with the iodinated organic compounds that iodism is not regarded as a causative agent.

The extensive use of iodophors as bactericidal agents in the milk industry of industrialized countries may conceivably raise the dietary iodine level above the optimum. Residues of the iodophors as now used may persist in milking units, transport equipment, and packaging devices. Proper monitoring can eliminate this possibility so that the iodine intake can be easily controlled.

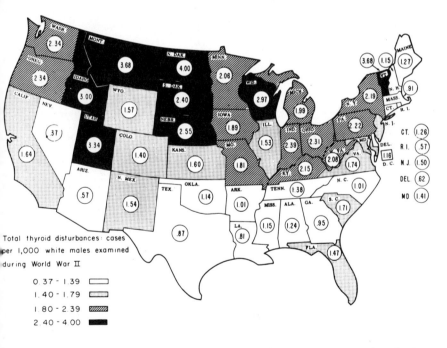

Figure 4. **Prevalence rates of total thyroid disturbances among white male Selective Service registrants during World War II: United States by states, 1940–1944 (from Pendergrast and others, 1961, with permission).**

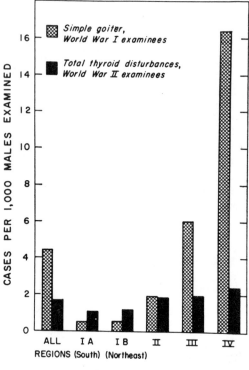

Figure 5. Prevalence rates of simple goiter among World War I male examinees and of total thyroid disturbances among World War II white male examinees: United States and regions as defined in Figure 3 (from Pendergrast and others, 1961, with permission).

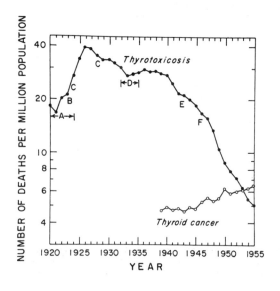

Figure 6. Crude mortality rates for thyrotoxicosis, 1920–1955, and for cancer of the thyroid, 1939–1955: Death registration states, 1920–1932; and United States, 1933–1955 (from Pendergrast and others, 1961, with permission). A. 1920–1924: Iodine used in some areas of the United States for prevention of goiter. B. 1923: Large doses of iodine advocated in preparing patients with toxic goiter for surgery. C. 1924 and 1928: Widespread campaigns advocating use of iodized salt for prevention of goiter. D. 1932 to 1935: Decrease in use of iodized salt during economic depression. E. 1943: Introduction of thiourea for the treatment of thyrotoxicosis. F. 1946: Introduction of radioiodine-131 for treatment of thyrotoxicosis.

Future Developments

The benefits of iodine therapy should be extended to many underdeveloped countries. In addition, more information is needed on substances that interfere with iodine metabolism and on problems of iodine metabolism itself (Pitt-Rivers and Trotter, 1964).

IRON

The medicinal use of iron began about 1,000 B.C. when the Egyptians and Greeks employed naturally occurring iron carbonates and oxides empirically, but successfully. Iron was administered for disease rather than for any definite disease entities. Even sexual impotency was treated with iron therapy. It was not until the 1700s that Lemery and Geoffry established the presence of iron in the ash of blood. From this was developed a more rational understanding of the role of iron in the body, although clinical comprehension of the good effects of iron therapy in the treatment of chlorosis dates from Sydenham in 1661. Recognition of the merits of ferrous over ferric iron began with the introduction of ferrous sulfate pills by Blaud in 1832.

Iron Metabolism

With the passage of years, therapy for iron lack has not changed greatly, and ferrous sulfate still is widely used. Iron is an essential constituent of hemoglobin, myoglobin, the cytochromes, and other enzyme systems involved in the transport and utilization of oxygen. Normal adults have an iron content ranging from 2 to 5 g, depending on body size and sex. Over 60 percent of the iron is present in circulating hemoglobin. Myoglobin accounts for a small percent of the iron. The remaining iron is stored chiefly in the liver, bone, and spleen, and these stores become very low in deficiency.

Current concepts on the absorption and utilization of ingested iron have been summarized by Moore (1961) in the schematic representation shown in Figure 7. To be absorbed, the 15 mg of iron ingested daily in the diet must be reduced to ferrous iron and chelated with ferritin, an organic moiety. This process takes place almost exclusively in the small intestine. People with lack of iron absorb iron more readily than do normals, but the mechanisms regulating the rate and amount of absorption are not understood. After iron reaches the blood plasma, it is oxidized to the ferric level and transported in combination with transferritin, a beta-l-globulin.

Once absorbed, iron can be stored to be used by the hematopoietic system, or it can be excreted as shown in Figure 7. Although the quantity of iron in the plasma is small, the turnover rate is rapid and amounts to 35 to 40 mg per day for the standard 70 kg man. Mammals have efficient ways of conserving iron, and relatively little iron is excreted in the normal course of events. Whenever red cells are lost by hemorrhage, the iron supply is depleted. In the standard man, the amount of iron stored amounts to 1 g, mainly in the form of the iron complexes ferritin and hemosiderin. Both complexes are mobilized to yield their iron if needed.

Toxicity

It was not until 1947 that a beginning was made in understanding the hazards of too much iron. Forbes (1947) reported on the accidental poisoning of small children, 2 to 4 years of age, by ferrous sulfate tablets prescribed for some adult member of the family, usually the mother. Because the mortality from acute iron poisoning is about 50 percent, this hazard has been studied from the point of view of epidemiology, pathology, treatment, and prevention (Aldrich, 1958). Although severe necrotizing gastritis is present in nearly every patient, the cause of death is cardiovascular collapse (Aldrich, 1958; Shafir, 1961). Mimicking the behavior of an adult seems to be the usual reason behind the ingestion of large numbers of iron tablets by children, but geophagia or "pica" may be an underlying cause in some instances.

Geophagia

The practice of eating dirt, clay, or charcoal is well established among a significant proportion of primitive and civilized people. To some, the underlying motivation

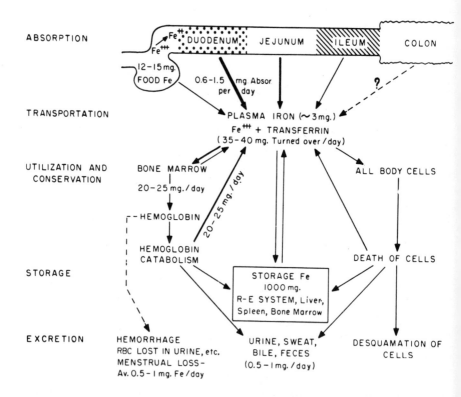

Figure 7. Simplified schematic outline of iron metabolism in the adult from Moore (1961). Extensive modification and expansion of this scheme are occurring as a result of more recent studies with radioisotopes and an appreciation of the many hemoglobinopathies.

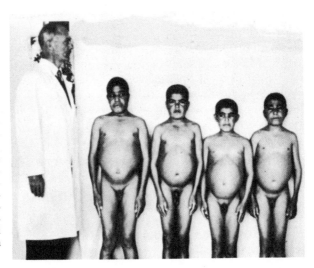

Figure 8. Clay-eaters from Iran illustrating the effects of geophagia. From left to right: Age 21, height 4 ft 11½ in.; age 18, height 4 ft, 9 in.; age 18, height 4 ft, 6 in.; age 21, height 4 ft, 7 in. All patients presented the following clinical features: severe iron deficiency anemia; hepatosplenomegaly; short stature; and marked hypogonadism (from Halsted and Prasad, 1960, with permission).

may be the urge to correct a deficiency state (Cooper, 1957). Publications by Halsted and Prasad (1960) and by Prasad and others (1961) on geophagia among Iranians have clearly demonstrated the hazards of habitual clay eating. Figure 8 shows four young men, age 18 to 21, who have eaten clay all their lives. The clay interfered with the absorption of minerals, especially iron, from the alimentary tract and thus produced severe iron-lack anemia, hypogonadism, dwarfism, and hepatosplenomegaly. A prolonged follow-up by Halsted and others (1972) on some of these patients after receiving a well-balanced diet indicated that the endocrine abnormalities of growth and sexual development are reversible.

Future Developments

Much more study must be done on iron therapy, metabolism, and toxicity. Iron therapy possibly should be converted to a public health measure through use of inorganic iron added to bread or of organic iron compounds added to salt or water. Information is needed particularly on iron absorption and metabolism (Forth and Rummel, 1973). Comparison of monographs published 15 years ago (such as Wallerstein and Mettier, 1958) with those currently in use (among others, Harris and Kellermeyer, 1970) shows that great advances have been made. But the unfolding field of the many hemoglobinopathies (Lehmann and Huntsman, 1972) indicates the need for knowledge about all the hemoglobins. Iron toxicity (Anonymous, 1961d; National Library of Medicine, 1968) similarly requires much more investigation because iron poisoning is frequent in infants and may be a serious problem in people with abnormal iron metabolism.

Although the study of iron and iron therapy is really a chapter in the history of the development of medicine, the advances have come rapidly in recent years through use of radioactive isotopes. Iron illustrates, as well as does any trace element, the problems involved in working out details of deficiency states, toxicity due to excess, and metabolic patterns.

FLUORINE

The use of fluoridated water as a means of inhibiting dental decay is still very new. In 1908, Frederick S. McKay, a dentist in Colorado, called the attention of his fellow dentists in the Colorado Springs area to the alarming incidence of mottled teeth in children—the so-called Colorado or Texas Stain. Through the years he established that drinking water in certain areas contained a substance that produced the stain and later showed that the same element inhibited dental decay.

Fluoride in Water

It was not until the depression that Churchill (1931) showed that the development of stained teeth in children correlated with high fluoride content of drinking water. In a sense, this discovery was anticipated a few years earlier by McCollum and others (1925) who found that fluorine altered the structure of rats' teeth and caused discoloration. Shortly after Churchill published his results, Smith and others (1931) reported that she and her colleagues had produced mottling of teeth in rats by feeding them fluorides.

Epidemiology

The U.S. Public Health Service was keenly interested in these developments, and in 1931, H. Trendly Dean, a dentist, was assigned to investigate the mottled-tooth problem. He began by sending questionnaires to the secretaries of local and national dental societies and by personally conducting field studies. Dean became interested in the minimal level at which fluoride was harmless and in the correlation of dental decay with the level of fluoride in drinking water. Dean conducted surveys in various localities, and by 1936 he was able to suggest that children with mottled teeth, from localities where there was more than 1 ppm of fluoride in the drinking water, had less tooth decay than children from fluoride-free areas (Dean, 1936). Later, Dean and others (1939) examined a large number of children in Quincy, Illinois, where the fluoride level of the water was 0.1 ppm and found they had more than three times as high a decay rate as an equal number of children from the nearby city of Galesburg, Illinois, where the fluoride level of the water supply was 1.8 ppm.

Mass Testing

Continued epidemiological studies brought Dean (1943) to the conclusion that the level of 1 ppm of fluoride in drinking water was safe for life-long consumption. With this assurance of safety, it remained only to conduct practical tests using two neighboring cities of about 50,000 population—one to add 1 ppm of fluoride to its water supply, and the other to serve as a control. History-making experiments were carried out in Michigan with Grand Rapids serving as the city with fluoridated water and Muskegon acting as the control, and a few months later in New York with Newburgh the fluoridated city and Kingston the control (Ast and others, 1950). The success of fluoridation in the prevention of dental decay was greater than expected, and within 5 years it was possible to show that fluoridation of drinking water at the level of 1 ppm reduced dental decay in growing children approximately 50 percent.

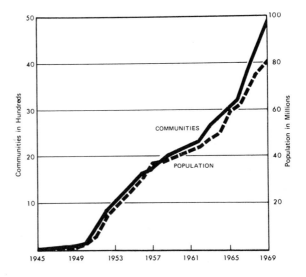

Figure 9. Communities and population served by controlled fluoridation in the United States, 1945–1969. Since natural fluoridated water is available to about 9.5 million people, the total was approximately 90 million (from Anonymous, 1969, *Fluoridation Census*, with permission).

In spite of the magnificent generalship shown in carrying out all stages of the fluoridation study program, acceptance by the public of water fluoridation is anything but uniform. Data published in the Public Health Reports for 1969 (reproduced in Fig. 9) show that the growth of fluoridation is following the standard "S" growth curve, so that 80 million drank controlled fluoridated water in 1969, but the rate of growth is flattening off.

Toxicity

It is well known that fluorides are toxic when ingested in any real concentration (Anonymous, 1961c). Accordingly, the World Health Organization has published a critical review on *Fluorides and Human Health* (1970). Long-continued exposure of workers in fluoride mines produces an osteosclerosis that interferes with the articulation of the joints and produces a stiff back (Roholm, 1937); conversely, lack of fluoride may produce osteoporosis (Anonymous, 1961b). There is great variation in the absorption and utilization of fluorides by individuals, and this idiosyncrasy has been used as an argument against fluoridation of public water supplies. Since alternative methods of protecting the teeth are available—such as fluoride tablets, fluoridized salt (Switzerland), fluoridized dentrifices, or topical application of fluoride solutions to the teeth—it is argued that fluoridation of public water supplies is an invasion of privacy. In any event, the issue is lively, and McNeil's book (McNeil, 1957) on fluoridation, although written in 1957, is still aptly entitled *The Fight for Fluoridation*.

Future Developments

Because consumption of fluoridated drinking water reduces dental decay only 50 percent, future investigations must be concerned with other factors that decrease or increase caries. Trace-element imbalances are being actively studied (Cannon and Hopps, 1971). Too much selenium may contribute to dental decay (Tank and Storvick, 1960), but this has not been confirmed by others. Calcium, magnesium, molybdenum, vanadium, and zinc are the elements most actively studied as protective metals.

SUMMARY

Some therapies to correct environmental element deficiencies and toxic excesses have been developed for soils, animals, and people, but much more must be done. Use of fertilizers, animal food additives, and human dietary ingredients have been discussed to point out the advances and to suggest future developments. The limited knowledge of the present must be greatly expanded to increase the yield of quality food products and to decrease the incidence of disease in plants, food animals, and man. Manipulation of fertilizers, food additives, and water composition offers great opportunities to accomplish these aims.

REFERENCES CITED

Aldrich, R. A., 1958, Acute iron toxicity, in Wallerstein, R. O., and Mettier, S. R., eds., Iron in clinical medicine: Berkeley and Los Angeles, Univ. California Press, p. 33–50.

Anke, M., and Groppel, B., 1970, Manganese deficiency and radioisotope studies on manganese metabolism, in Mills, C. F., ed., Trace element metabolism in animals: Edinburgh and London, E. & S. Livingstone, p. 133–136.

Anonymous, 1961a, Relation of endemic goiter to thyroid carcinoma and thyrotoxicosis: Nutrition Reviews, v. 19, p. 166–167.

——1961b, Bone density and fluoride ingestion: Nutrition Reviews, v. 19, p. 198–199.

——1961c, Metabolism of fluorides: Nutrition Reviews, v. 19, p. 259–262.

——1961d, Ferrous-sulphate poisoning in childhood: Lancet, v. 1, p. 869–870.

——1969, Fluoridation census: Bethesda, Maryland, Div. Dental Health, Public Health Service, U.S. Dept. Health, Education and Welfare, 72 p.

——1971, Absorption of dietary iron in man: Nutrition Reviews, v. 29, p. 113–115.

Ast, D., Finn, S. B., and McCaffrey, I., 1950, The Newburgh-Kingston caries-fluorine study: Am. Jour. Pub. Health, v. 40, p. 716–724.

Astwood, E. B., Sullivan, J., Bissell, A., and Tyslowitz, R., 1943, Action of certain sulfonamides and of thiourea upon the function of the thyroid gland: Endocrinology, v. 32, p. 210–225.

Baumann, E., 1896, Über den Jodgehalt der Schilddrüsen von Menschen und Tieren (III. Mitteilung): Hoppe Seylers, Zool. Physiol. Chem., v. 22, p. 1–17.

Berg, J. W., and Burbank, F., 1972, Correlations between carcinogenic trace metals in water supplies and cancer mortality: New York Acad. Sci. Annals, v. 199, p. 249–264.

Cannon, H. L., and Hopps, H. C., eds., 1971, Environmental geochemistry in health and disease: Geol. Soc. America Mem. 123, 230 p.

Chatin, A., 1852, Recherche de l'iode dans l'air, les eaux, le sol et les produits alimentaires des Alpes de la France et du Piémont: Acad. Sci. Comptes Rendus, v. 34, p. 14–18, 51–54.

Churchill, H. V., 1931, The occurrence of fluorides in some waters of the United States: Am. Water Works Assoc. Jour., v. 23, p. 1399–1407.

Coindet, J. R., 1820, Découverte d'un nouveau remède courte le goitre: Ann. Chim. Phys., v. 15, p. 49–59.

Cooper, M., 1957, Pica: Springfield, Ill., Charles C Thomas, 114 p.

Dean, H. T., 1936, Chronic endemic dental fluorosis: Am. Med. Assoc. Jour., v. 107, p. 1269–1273.

——1943, Domestic water and dental caries: Am. Water Works Assoc. Jour., v. 35, p. 1161–11.

Dean, H. T., and Elvove, E., 1935, Studies on the minimal threshold of the dental sign of chronic endemic fluorosis (mottled enamel): Public Health Rept., v. 50, p. 1719–1729.

Dean, H. T., Jay, P., Arnold, F. A., Jr., McClure, F., and Elvove, E., 1939, Domestic water and dental caries including certain epidemiological aspects of oral *L. acidolphus:* Public Health Rept., v. 54, p. 862–888.

Epstein, E., 1971, Mineral nutrition of plants: Principles and perspectives: New York, John Wiley & Sons, Inc., 412 p.

Fassett, D. W., 1966, Nitrites and nitrates: Natl. Acad. Sci., Natl. Research Council Pub., no. 1354, p. 250–256.

Fellenburg, T. von, 1926, Das Vorkommen, der Kreislauf und der Stoffwechsel des Jods.: Ergeb. Physiol., v. 25, p. 176–363.

Fluorides and Human Health, 1970, Contributors, Adler, P., and others, Prepared in consultation with ninety-three dental and medical specialists in various countries: Geneva, Switzerland, World Health Organization, Mon. Ser., no. 59, 364 p.

Forbes, G., 1947, Poisoning with a preparation of iron, copper, and manganese: British Med. Jour., v. 1, p. 367–370.

Forth, W., and Rummel, W., 1973, Iron absorption: Physiological Reviews, v. 53, p. 724–792.

Gross, J., and Pitt-Rivers, R., 1952, The identification of 3.5:3'-l-triiodothyronine in human plasma: Lancet, v. 1, p. 439–441.

Halsted, J. A., and Prasad, A. S., 1960, Syndrome of iron deficiency anemia, hepatosplenomegaly, hypogonadism, dwarfism, and geophagia: Am. Clin. Climatol. Assoc. Trans., v. 72, p. 130–149.

Halsted, J. A., Ronaghy, H. A., Abadi, P., Haghshenass, M., Amirhakemi, G. H., Barakat, R. M., and Reinhold, J. G., 1972, Zinc deficiency in man. The Shiraz experiment: Am. Jour. Med., v. 53, p. 277–284.

Harington, C. R., 1926, Chemistry of thyroxine. II. Constitution and synthesis of desiodothyroxine: Biochem. Jour., v. 20, p. 300–313.

Harington, C. R., and Barger, G., 1927, Chemistry of thyroxine. III. Constitution and synthesis of thyroxine: Biochem. Jour., v. 21, p. 169–183.

Harris, J. W., and Kellermeyer, R. W., 1970, The red cell—Production, metabolism, destruction: Normal and abnormal: Cambridge, Mass., Harvard Univ. Press, 795 p.

Hennig, A., 1972, Mineralstoffe, Vitamine, Ergotropika: Berlin, DDR, VEB Deutsch. Landwirtschaftsverlag, 636 p.

Hird, F.J.R., and Trikojus, V. M., 1948, Paper partition chromatography with thyroxine analogues: Australian Jour. Sci., v. 10, p. 185–187.

Kendall, E. C., 1919, Isolation of iodine compound which occurs in the thyroid: Jour. Biol. Chem., v. 39, p. 125–132.

Kimball, O. P., 1939, Twenty years in the prevention of goiter (1916–1936): Ohio State Med. Jour., v. 35, p. 705–709.

Kohl, D. H., Shearer, G. B., and Commoner, B., 1971, Fertilizer nitrogen: Contribution to nitrate in surface water in a corn belt watershed: Science, v. 174, p. 1331–1334.

Lehmann, H., and Huntsman, R. G., 1972, The hemoglobinopathies, *in* Stansbury, J. B., Wyngaarden, J., and Frederickson, D. S., eds., The metabolic basis of inherited disease: New York, McGraw-Hill Book Co., p. 1398–1431.

Lenihan, J.M.A., 1967, Technology and humanity, *in* Proceedings of the University of Missouri's 1st Annual Conference on Trace Substances in Environmental Health: Columbia, Univ. Missouri, p. 141–151.

Marine, D., and Kimball, O. P., 1921, The prevention of simple goiter in man: Am. Med. Assoc. Jour., v. 77, p. 1068–1070.

McCollum, E. V., Simmonds, N., and Becker, J. E., 1925, The effect of addition of fluorine to the diet of the rat on the quality of the teeth: Jour. Biol. Chem., v. 63, p. 553–562.

McNeil, D. R., 1957, The fight for fluoridation: New York, Oxford Press, 241 p.

Mertz, W., and Cornatzer, W. E., eds., 1971, Newer trace elements in nutrition: New York, Marcel Dekker, Inc., 438 p

Miller, J. K., Moss, B. R., Swanson, E. W., Aschbacher, P. W., and Craige, R. G., 1967, Calcium iodate and pentacalcium orthoperiodate as sources of supplemental iodine for cattle: Jour. Dairy Sci., v. 51, p. 1831–1835.

Miller, M. W., and Berg, G. G., 1969, Chemical fallout: Springfield, Ill., Charles C Thomas, 531 p.

Miller, M. W., and Clarkson, T. W., 1972, Mercury, mercurials and mercaptans: Springfield, Ill., Charles C Thomas, 420 p.

Mills, C. F., ed., 1970, Trace element metabolism in animals: Edinburgh and London, E. & S. Livingstone, 550 p.

Moore, C. V., 1961, Iron metabolism and nutrition, Harvey Lectures, Ser. 55, 1959–1960: New York, New York Acad. Medicine, p. 67–101.

National Library of Medicine, 1968, Untoward Effects of Iron. Mid-1963–Sept. 1967 (178 citations): Literature Search No. 8–68: Bethesda, Md., 4 p.

National Research Council, Committee on Animal Nutrition, 1968a, Number 5: Nutrient requirements of sheep: Washington, D.C., Natl. Acad. Sci., 64 p.

——1968b, Number 2: Nutrient requirements of swine: Washington, D.C., Natl. Acad. Sci., 69 p.

——1970, Number 4: Nutrient requirements of beef cattle: Washington, D.C., Natl. Acad. Sci., 55 p.

——1971a, Number 3: Nutrient requirements of dairy cattle: Washington, D.C., Natl. Acad. Sci., 54 p.

——1971b, Number 1: Nutrient requirements of poultry: Washington, D.C., Natl. Acad. Sci., 54 p.

Oswald, A., 1899, Die Eiweisskoerper der Schilddruese: Hoppe Seylers, Zool. Physiol. Chem., v. 27, p. 14–20.

Pendergrast, W. J., Milmore, B. K., and Marcus, S. C., 1961, Thyroid cancer and thyrotoxicosis in the United States: Their relation to endemic goiter: Jour. Chronic Disease, v. 13, p. 22–38.

Pitt-Rivers, R., and Trotter, W. R., eds., 1964, The thyroid gland: London, Butterworth, v. I, 442 p., v. II, 325 p.

Prasad, A. S., Halsted, J. A., and Nadimi, M., 1961, Syndrome of iron deficiency anemia, hepatosplenomegaly, hypogonadism, dwarfism, and geophagia: Am. Med. Jour., v. 31, p. 532–546.

Prince, A. L., 1957, Trace element delivering capacity of 10 New Jersey soil types as measured by spectrographic analyses of soils and mature corn leaves: Soil Science, v. 84, p. 413–418.

Rawson, R. W., Hertz, S., and Means, J. H., 1943, Thiocyanate goiter in man: Int. Med. Annal., v. 19, p. 829–842.

Rice, C. O., 1938, Histologic structure of normal thyroid gland: Arch. Surgery, v. 36, p. 96–110.

Roholm, K., 1937, Fluorine intoxication: London, Lewis, 364 p.

Sauer, H. I., 1962, Epidemiology of cardiovascular mortality—Geographic and ethnic: Am. Jour. Pub. Health, v. 52, p. 94–105.

Scott, M. L., Nesheim, M. C., and Young, R. J., 1969, Nutrition of the chicken: Ithaca, New York, M. L. Scott & Associates, 511 p.

Scrimshaw, N. S., 1957, Endemic goiter: Nutrition Rev., v. 15, p. 161–164.

Shafir, M., 1961, The management of acute poisoning by ferrous sulfate: Pediatrics, v. 27, p. 83–94.

Smith, M. C., Lantz, E. M., and Smith, H. V., 1931, The cause of mottled enamel, a defect of human teeth: Science, v. 74, p. 244.

Tank, G., and Storvick, C. A., 1960, Effect of naturally occurring selenium and vanadium on dental caries: Dental Research Jour., v. 39, p. 473–488.

Underwood, E. J., 1972, Trace elements in human and animal nutrition, 3rd ed.: New York and London, Academic Press, Inc., 543 p.

United States Public Health Service, 1963, Cancer control program, age-adjusted and age-specific death rates for malignant neoplasms. 1960: Public Health Serv. Pub., no. 1113, 113 p.

Wallerstein, R. O., and Mettier, S. R., eds., 1958, Iron in clinical medicine: Berkeley and Los Angeles, Univ. California Press, 283 p.

World Health Organization, 1960, Monograph Ser. No. 44, Endemic goiter: Prevalence and geographical distribution of endemic goiter: Geneva, World Health Organization, 471 p.

PAPER PRESENTED AT THE 1972 ANNUAL MEETING OF THE GEOLOGICAL SOCIETY OF AMERICA IN MINNEAPOLIS, MINNESOTA

MANUSCRIPT RECEIVED BY THE SOCIETY FEBRUARY 2, 1974

Geological Society of America
Special Paper 155
© 1975

Sampling Designs in Environmental Geochemistry

HARRY A. TOURTELOT

AND

A. T. MIESCH
U.S. Geological Survey
Federal Center
Denver, Colorado 80225

ABSTRACT

Growing demand for geochemical surveys of large areas for environmental purposes involves costs and technical rigor that necessitate increased concern for sampling design. In order to supply data for which the degree of uncertainty is known and to use both field and laboratory resources efficiently, formal experimental design procedures must be used. Optimum final sampling designs can be determined only from the results of preliminary pilot studies in which analysis of variance techniques is a powerful tool.

Analysis of variance techniques can be applied to the study of conceptual units that make up the landscape (such as rock units, soils, plant communities, and hydrologic units) or to areal studies of undifferentiated surface materials. The techniques applied to data from a pilot study provide estimates of the total geochemical variation: for example, of a shale unit as a whole and of the variation among (1) stratigraphic sections of the shale, (2) major parts of the sections sampled, (3) the samples themselves, and (4) duplicate analyses of the samples. From these results, a final sampling plan can be designed that includes an adequate density of sampling, in both geographic and stratigraphic senses, and independent information on the precision of analytical methods, as well as information on the adequacy of this precision for the problem at hand. In addition, comparison of the variance among mean values for either conceptual subunits or areal units with the error variance associated with the mean values gives insight to the reproducibility of the differences observed among the mean values. The reproducibility of such differences can be brought to almost any desired degree of confidence by adjusting the sampling plan so that the variance of each mean is small compared with the variance between the means. Once it has been determined that the data at hand will adequately describe differences in concentrations of elements, background geochemical maps of known reliability can be made. The expectable 68 and 95 percent ranges in composition permit confident recognition of extreme values.

Examples of the application of analysis of variance techniques are given for the study of the composition of uncultivated soils in vegetation type areas in Missouri and for undifferentiated surface materials in the Front Range Urban Corridor of Colorado.

INTRODUCTION

The importance and significance of contributions from the field of environmental geochemistry to the health and well-being of man are going to be examined closely by the nongeochemists who have to make the cultural and political decisions necessary to preserve and improve our environment. As pointed out by Angino (1971) and Congressman McCloskey (1971), the data for these control decisions must be provided by geochemists. It is necessary and important for geochemists not only to supply data but to supply data for which the degree of uncertainty is known. This is underscored by the following points:

1. Because legislative or other decisions based on geochemical data may affect the well-being of the general public, the data must be statistically defensible before the general scientific community.

2. Misleading data or misuse of data may affect the credibility of all geochemical research so that geochemistry may not play the full role in environmental decisions that it should.

3. Inadequate qualifications of geochemical data may lead to unreasonable control decisions that may compromise the well-being of the public or impose needless burdens on the economic functions of the nation.

It therefore seems absolutely necessary to conduct surveys in environmental geochemistry with the utmost rigor, and this requires the use of formal experimental designs.

EXPERIMENTAL DESIGNS

The use of formal experimental designs insures the necessary technical rigor needed in environmental geochemical surveys and provides for the most efficient use of field time, laboratory capabilities, and financial resources.

Formal experimental design procedures have not been used extensively in field geochemistry, but some work is prominent. W. J. Youden, statistician, and A. Mehlich, soil scientist, collaborated in a study of the regional variation in soil pH over large areas using an analysis of variance model (Youden and Mehlich, 1937). Nearly 20 years later, Krumbein and Slack (1956) used a formal statistical design to examine regional variation in the radioactivity of a black shale unit. Krumbein and Slack were also able to show how formal statistical designs can be used to improve efficiency and to obtain geochemical results of known reliability. Chemical variation in some crystalline rocks of the San Bernardino Mountains of California

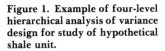

Figure 1. Example of four-level hierarchical analysis of variance design for study of hypothetical shale unit.

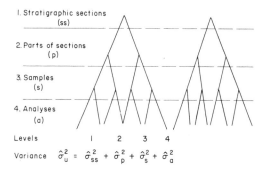

1. Stratigraphic sections (ss)

2. Parts of sections (p)

3. Samples (s)

4. Analyses (a)

Levels   1   2   3   4

Variance $\hat{\sigma}_u^2 = \hat{\sigma}_{ss}^2 + \hat{\sigma}_p^2 + \hat{\sigma}_s^2 + \hat{\sigma}_a^2$

has been described by Baird and others (1967a, 1967b).

Formal experimental design procedures are easily applied to the two principal kinds of environmental geochemical investigations—landscape studies and problem studies—but this discussion deals only with landscape studies.

A four-level hierarchical analysis of variance design for the study of a shale unit is represented in Figure 1, but any conceptual unit in the landscape could be used. A conceptual unit is simply an aggregate of materials that has a homogeneity based on criteria that must be defined by the investigator. Many environmental units, however, have a natural homogeneity, such as lithologic types, ground waters from particular aquifers, soil types, or areas of characteristic vegetation.

The design shown here permits the estimation of the total geochemical variation in the shale unit; the variance among stratigraphic sections (level 1), major parts of the sampled stratigraphic sections (level 2), the samples themselves (level 3), and duplicate analyses of the samples (level 4). Details of the calculations for computing variance components such as these can be found in statistical text books (Anderson and Bancroft, 1952), but the calculations are particularly well illustrated by Krumbein and Slack (1956). All variances considered in this paper are computed in terms of $\log_{10}$ concentration values. The significant feature of variance components is that, if biases in sampling and analysis are absent (Miesch, 1967), the variances at levels 1 to 4 are additive and their sum is equal to the total variance of the shale unit as a whole. It is possible to determine the percentage of variance contributed by each level of the design for each chemical element involved in the study (Fig. 2).

Geochemically coherent elements tend to behave similarly within a given study and three diverse behaviors are illustrated. For element X, relatively little variance appears between stratigraphic sections and between duplicate analyses, only 10 and 20 percent, respectively. The remainder of the variance (70 percent) appears up and down the stratigraphic column between major parts of the sections and between samples at the sampling sites. Among the inferences to be drawn with respect to any final sampling plans for this element in this unit are the following:

1. The total rock unit is very similar from place to place within the area of interest. As much can be learned by sampling in only a few stratigraphic sections as by sampling in many.

2. The analytical method accounts for only a small part of the total variation in the data. A more precise method would neither greatly reduce the total variation

Shale unit		Stratigraphic sections		Parts of sections		Samples		Analyses
Levels	=	1		2		3		4
Variance $\hat{\sigma}_u^2$	=	$\hat{\sigma}_{ss}^2$	+	$\hat{\sigma}_p^2$	+	$\hat{\sigma}_s^2$	+	$\hat{\sigma}_a^2$
Element X 100	=	10	+	30	+	40	+	20%
Element Y 100	=	60	+	20	+	10	+	10%
Element Z 100	=	10	+	20	+	10	+	60%

Figure 2. Contributions of variance by levels for three chemical elements in hypothetical shale unit.

in the data nor improve the estimated variation in the rock unit.

3. The relatively large amount of variation between the upper and lower parts of the stratigraphic section may confirm what might have been obvious on the outcrop from observation of lithologic character.

4. The 40 percent variation between samples within parts of the stratigraphic sections indicates large variation over small stratigraphic intervals. This, too, may have been apparent at the outcrop, but there is now a measure of its relative importance.

Because the variation in element X is concentrated within the stratigraphic column, at both large and small scales, this shale unit could thus be described almost as adequately by a moderately detailed study of a few stratigraphic sections anywhere in the outcrop belt as by studying numerous sections. The greater efficiency in this is obvious.

The distribution of element Y in the shale unit, however, is different from that of element X. The major part of the variation reflects the differences between stratigraphic sections. To describe the distribution of element Y in this shale unit, stratigraphic sections from the entire study area must be investigated. Results of detailed studies of only a few sections would not be applicable to the shale unit in its entirety.

Element Z is also different. Here, the bulk of the variation is contributed by the analytical method. This variation is so large that only limited inferences can be drawn about the actual variation in the unit itself. When this situation is found, the only alternative is to use a more precise analytical method.

Plans for the final sampling of the shale unit can now go ahead on the basis of this information. The final plan either will focus on a few elements of interest that behave similarly or will be a compromise that adequately treats a number of elements that behave differently.

Further use of analysis of variance procedures is best illustrated by the example that follows.

The U.S. Geological Survey is in the final year of a four-year study of environmental geochemistry in the state of Missouri (U.S. Geol. Survey, 1969). The objective of the work has been to provide estimates, of known reliability, of the mean composition and natural variation for the major units of the

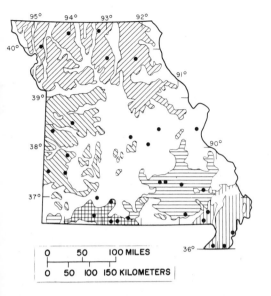

EXPLANATION OF
VEGETATION TYPE AREAS

▨ Glaciated prairie

▨ Unglaciated prairie

☐ Oak-hickory forest

▤ Oak-hickory-pine forest

▦ Cedar glade

▥ Floodplain forest

● Location of quadrangles
   that were sampled

Figure 3. Distribution of vegetation type areas in Missouri and quadrangles sampled in each type (modified from Shacklette and others, 1970).

environment in support of epidemiological research undertaken by the Environmental Health Center of the University of Missouri. As part of this work, the B horizon of uncultivated soils within each vegetation type area of the state was sampled (Fig. 3) to obtain, in part, information on the natural compositional variation of such soils (Shacklette and others, 1970).

A hierarchical analysis of variance design was used to study compositional variation in the soil. The design of the pilot study consisted of five quadrangles selected at random from each of the six vegetation type areas (dots in Fig. 3). Within each quadrangle, samples were collected at two randomly selected sites for a total of 60 samples. The analysis of variance design consists of three levels (Fig. 4).

Variance in soil composition is estimated between vegetation type areas (level 1), between quadrangles within areas (level 2), and between sample sites within quadrangles (level 3). As shown at the bottom of Figure 4, the total compositional variance of soils in Missouri is the sum of the variance between vegetation type areas plus the variance between quadrangles within areas plus the variance between

Figure 4. Schematic three-level hierarchical analysis of variance for study of soils in Missouri vegetation type areas.

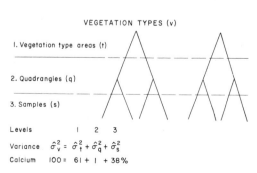

VEGETATION TYPES (v)

1. Vegetation type areas (t)

2. Quadrangles (q)

3. Samples (s)

Levels   1   2   3

Variance $\hat{\sigma}_v^2 = \hat{\sigma}_t^2 + \hat{\sigma}_q^2 + \hat{\sigma}_s^2$

Calcium $100 = 61 + 1 + 38\%$

sample sites within the quadrangles. The analytical variance was not estimated separately and, so, is contained in the third and final term in this illustration. The percentage contribution of each level for calcium also is shown on Figure 4. A 61 percent variation exists between the areas, and at least some of the areas are distinctively different in calcium when compared to the others. On the other hand, soils within any given vegetation type area are relatively uniform in their calcium content because the variance among quadrangles is small.

What if the differences, however, among areas were not so striking? The variance among the areas ($\hat\sigma_t^2$) estimates the variation among their means. Yet each area mean is itself only an estimate and, thus, is subject to error. The areal differences to be shown on any map are valid only to the extent that the error associated with each mean is sufficiently small compared to the differences observed among the means. In this case, the error variance of the mean can be estimated from the last two terms of the variance equation.

The log variance of nickel among soils in the six vegetation type areas was estimated as 0.0119 (Shacklette and others, 1971) as shown on line 1 of Figure 5, and this represents the magnitude of the differences among the six area means. The error variance associated with these means is a function of the variance at the two lower levels of the design and the number of items selected for sampling at those levels. The error variance is estimated as 0.00736, only slightly smaller than the variance among the means, the ratio between the variance among the areas, and the error variance being about 1.6. That is, the error in estimating a mean is nearly as great as the differences observed among the means. The absolute minimum acceptable value of this ratio is about 1.0 (Connor and others, 1972, p. 9), and if the geochemical pattern of a particular element (such as nickel) is important environmentally, it seems reasonable to try to achieve a greater stability in differences among the six means than that indicated by a ratio of 1.6.

A second stage of sampling was planned involving more quadrangles and sampling sites, because if these items are increased, the error in estimation of the means will be reduced. The probable effect on this error of sampling in 10 quadrangles per vegetation type area and of collecting five samples per quadrangle is shown in line 2 of Figure 5, where the variance ratio resulting from such a design potentially will be about 6.

This second stage of sampling resulted in 300 samples, and the variances estimated from these data are shown in line 3 of Figure 5 (Shacklette and others, 1971). The variance based on 300 samples is not identical with that based on 60 samples

$\hat\sigma_t^2$	$\hat\sigma_{\bar x}^2$		$\dfrac{\hat\sigma_q^2}{n_q}$	$+$	$\dfrac{\hat\sigma_s^2}{n_q n_s}$	($n_q = 5 : n_s = 2$)
1. 0.0119	0.00736	$=$	$\dfrac{0.0193}{5}$	$+$	$\dfrac{0.035}{5 \times 2}$	
2. 0.0119	0.002	$=$	$\dfrac{0.0193}{10}$	$+$	$\dfrac{0.035}{10 \times 5}$	($n_q = 10 : n_s = 5$)
3. 0.0286	0.00264	$=$	$\dfrac{0.0156}{10}$	$+$	$\dfrac{0.0541}{10 \times 5}$	

Figure 5. Comparison of log variance of nickel concentrations in soils of Missouri vegetation type areas ($\hat\sigma_t^2$) and standard error of the means ($\hat\sigma_{\bar x}^2$). Line 1: results from preliminary sampling plan. Line 2: estimate of effect of modifying preliminary sampling plan. Line 3: results of second-stage sampling plan (Shacklette and others, 1971).

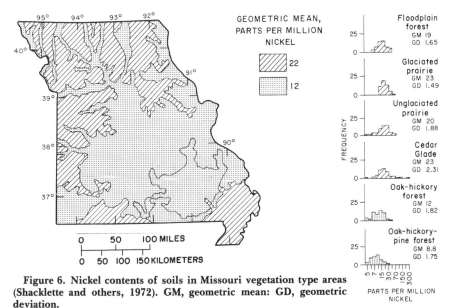

Figure 6. Nickel contents of soils in Missouri vegetation type areas (Shacklette and others, 1972). GM, geometric mean: GD, geometric deviation.

but it is not greatly different (0.0286 versus 0.0119). More importantly, the ratio between the area variance and the error variance estimated from the new data is now about 10 rather than 6, as predicted.

With the statistical demonstration that these new data adequately describe differences in the mean concentration of nickel in soils of the six vegetation type areas in Missouri, maps (such as Fig. 6) can be prepared (Shacklette and others, 1972). A statistical procedure based on Duncan's Multiple Range Test (Duncan, 1955) was used to identify significant differences among individual means. (See below for further discussion of the Duncan test.) Maps, such as Figure 6, define background concentrations and may be used to assess the general geochemical characteristics of any local area in Missouri. The expectable 68 and 95 percent ranges in composition based on the mean composition and the variance will allow confident recognition of extreme values.

The emphasis of the work in Missouri was on the natural landscape, particularly the rural one. However, the potential geochemical effects of urbanization on the landscape constitute an area of research that is bound to become more important.

Such an investigation is underway as part of the Geological Survey's environmental studies of the Front Range Urban Corridor of Colorado, an area of about 11,000 km² that includes Denver and adjacent areas, which are likely to develop into a megalopolis in the future (Fig. 7). In contrast to the work in Missouri, the Front Range area sampling plan was based on regularly spaced rather than randomly selected sampling areas, and samples were taken at the surface without consideration of the earth materials involved.

A pilot investigation was conducted involving 12 of the 74 7½′ quadrangles that make up the total area. The pilot area contains about 1,800 km² and includes

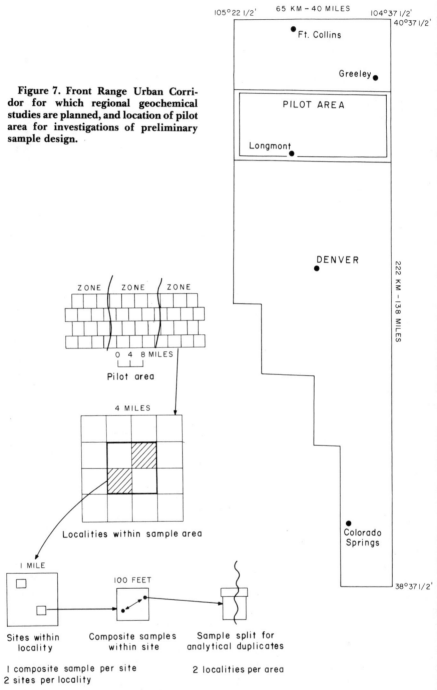

Figure 7. Front Range Urban Corridor for which regional geochemical studies are planned, and location of pilot area for investigations of preliminary sample design.

105°22 1/2'   65 KM — 40 MILES   104°37 1/2'
40°37 1/2'

● Ft. Collins

Greeley ●

PILOT AREA

Longmont ●

DENVER ●

222 KM — 138 MILES

● Colorado Springs

38°37 1/2'

ZONE   ZONE   ZONE

0 4 8 MILES
Pilot area

4 MILES

Localities within sample area

I MILE

100 FEET

Sites within locality

Composite samples within site

Sample split for analytical duplicates

I composite sample per site
2 sites per locality

2 localities per area

Figure 8. Preliminary sample design in pilot area study of the Front Range Urban Corridor.

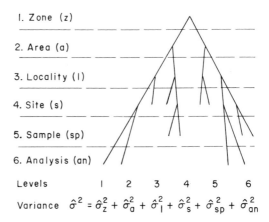

Figure 9. Six-level hierarchical analysis of variance design for regional geochemical investigations of surficial materials in Front Range Urban Corridor pilot area.

1. Zone (z)

2. Area (a)

3. Locality (l)

4. Site (s)

5. Sample (sp)

6. Analysis (an)

Levels   1   2   3   4   5   6

Variance $\hat{\sigma}^2 = \hat{\sigma}_z^2 + \hat{\sigma}_a^2 + \hat{\sigma}_l^2 + \hat{\sigma}_s^2 + \hat{\sigma}_{sp}^2 + \hat{\sigma}_{an}^2$

a good representation of the surficial materials likely to be found in the total area.

The pilot area was divided into three zones (Fig. 8). The zones were further subdivided into areas of 16 mi² each, giving a total of 42 areas. Two 1-mi² localities were then randomly selected from the central 4 mi² of each area, and two sites, each 100 ft sq, were selected randomly from each locality. Samples were collected at each of two randomly selected spots within each site. The two samples in most sites were composited into a single sample, thus reducing the analytical workload. Thirty randomly chosen samples were split into two equal parts in order to measure the variance arising in the laboratory. All samples, including the duplicates, were submitted to the laboratory in a randomized sequence and were analyzed in that order. Any systematic errors in the analytical procedures are thus effectively transformed into random errors.

This plan results in the six-level hierarchical analysis of variance design (Fig. 9). For each chemical element, inferences can be drawn as to the geographic scale of variation, because the variance between samples reflects variation at distances as great as 30 m (100 ft), variance between sites reflects variation at distances of ~ 30 m (100 ft) to 1.6 km (1 mi), variance between localities reflects variation at distances as much as 1.6 to 3.2 km, variance between areas reflects variation from several to 24 km (15 mi), and variance between zones reflects variation at distances greater than about 24 km (15 mi).

The results for nickel are shown in Figure 10. There is almost as much variation, 22 percent of the total log variance, between any two sampling sites within 1 mi² as there is between the areas, 27 percent, which are separated by distances of as much as 15 mi. Only 1 percent of the variation for nickel and only a few percent for most of the other elements occur between localities. This implies that adequate results would be obtained if only one 1-mi² locality instead of two had been sampled in each area.

The log variance, 0.03577, of nickel between areas is about three times the error variance, 0.01201, encountered in estimating the area means. This factor of three appears to be large enough (Connor and others, 1972, p. 9) to insure a reasonable stability in the difference among area means. Duncan's Multiple

Zones	Areas	Localities	Sites	Samples	Analyses
$\hat{\sigma}^2 = \hat{\sigma}_z^2$	$+ \;\; \hat{\sigma}_a^2$	$+ \;\; \hat{\sigma}_l^2$	$+ \;\; \hat{\sigma}_s^2$	$+ \;\; \hat{\sigma}_{sp}^2$	$+ \;\; \hat{\sigma}_{an}^2$
100	$+ \;\; 27$	$+ \;\; 1$	$+ \;\; 22$	$+ \;\; 15$	$+ \;$ 9 percent

$$\hat{\sigma}_{\bar{x}}^2 = \frac{\hat{\sigma}_l^2}{n_l} + \frac{\hat{\sigma}_s^2}{n_l n_s} + \frac{\hat{\sigma}_{sp}^2}{n_l n_s n_{sp}} + \frac{\hat{\sigma}_{an}^2}{n_l n_s n_{sp} n_{an}}$$

$$\hat{\sigma}_a^2 = 0.03577 \qquad 0.01201 = \frac{0.00161}{2} + \frac{0.02920}{2 \times 2} \quad \frac{0.01936}{2 \times 2 \times 2} \quad \frac{0.01185}{2 \times 2 \times 2 \times 1}$$

Figure 10. Results of analysis of variance for nickel in pilot study of Front Range Urban Corridor.

Range Test (Duncan, 1955) has been used to judge the minimum difference required before any two area means may be considered to be significantly different.

The square root of the error variance (0.01201, Fig. 10) is 0.11; this is the standard error attached to any area mean. At least four samples (two in each locality) were collected and analyzed from each area, but because the estimated variance between localities is nearly zero, the four samples may be viewed as four randomly located samples. Thus, if 3 degrees of freedom are assigned to each area, the standard error is based on at least 126 degrees of freedom (42 areas × 3). Duncan's Table II (Duncan, 1955) can be entered with n (degrees of freedom) = 100 and p (number of means being compared) = 50, and a significant studentized range of 3.53 for the 5 percent probability level is found. However, the values of n and p are hardly critical. For $p = 50$, the studentized range extends only from 3.47 to 3.61 for values of n ranging from 13 to infinity.

Multiplying the value of 3.53 by the log standard error of the area means (0.11), we find a shortest significant range of 0.38. The antilogarithm of this value is approximately 2.4, and because all computations are based on logarithms of concentration values, 2.4 may then be called the lowest significant factor. Thus, area means differing by a factor of 2.4 or more may be regarded as significantly different at the 95 percent level of confidence. Centering the range based on this factor around the geometric mean of 7.9 ppm is a convenient way to distinguish areas of high and low values that are significantly different. The pattern illustrated in Figure 11 was arrived at in this manner. Note that the higher boundary value, 12.2 ppm, is larger than the lower boundary value, 5.1 ppm, by a factor of 2.4, and that 12.2/7.9 approximately equals 7.9/5.1.

The area of generally high values on Figure 11 corresponds with the outcrop of predominantly clayey rocks of Cretaceous age, even though most samples are of surficial materials. The area of low values in the west falls within the outcrop of crystalline rocks of Precambrian age and quartzose rocks of late Paleozoic and early Mesozoic ages. The area of low values in the east corresponds partly to the flood plain of the South Platte River but corresponds chiefly to an area of sand hills to the east.

The analysis of variance indicates that the samples collected are satisfactory for describing compositional differences among sample areas for most of the elements of environmental interest, including cobalt, copper, lead, lithium, selenium, vanadium, and zinc. On the other hand, the analysis of variance indicates

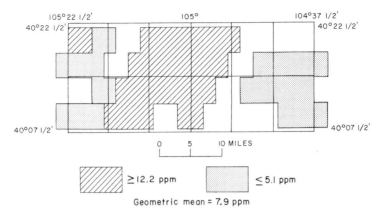

Figure 11. Nickel concentrations in sample areas from pilot study of Front Range Urban Corridor.

that compositional differences between areas cannot be described for silicon, titanium, and phosphorus without increasing the number of samples taken and, hence, increasing the cost beyond limits that can be justified in the present state of knowledge. For elements of most interest, the sampling design seems suitable for expansion to cover the entire Front Range Urban Corridor; this work is underway.

In conclusion, the use of formal experimental designs follows the lead of Youden and Mehlich (1937) and of Krumbein and Slack (1956). The reasons why such formal designs have not been used more extensively in field geochemistry are obscure. Perhaps the fundamental reason is that formal designs have not been demanded by geochemists. In presenting results to environmentalists of other professions, however, this will not be the case. The use of formal experimental designs will enable us to produce results that will be statistically defensible and that are compatible with other environmental data.

REFERENCES CITED

Anderson, R. L., and Bancroft, T. A., 1952, Statistical theory in research: New York, McGraw-Hill Book Co., Inc., 399 p.

Angino, E. E., 1971, Environmental geochemistry, politics, and reality: Geol. Soc. America, Abs. with Programs, v. 3, no. 7, p. 493–494.

Baird, A. K., McIntyre, D. B., and Welday, E. E., 1967a, Geochemical and structural studies in batholithic rocks of southern California—Pt. II, Sampling of the Rattlesnake Mountain pluton for chemical composition, variability, and trend analysis: Geol. Soc. America Bull., v. 78, p. 199–222.

——1967b, A test of chemical variability and field sampling methods, Lakeview Mountain tonalite, Lakeview Mountains, southern California Batholith: California Div. Mines and Geology Spec. Rept. 92, p. 11–19.

Connor, J. J., Feder, G. L., Erdman, J. A., and Tidball, R. R., 1972, Environmental geochemistry in Missouri—A multidisciplinary study: Symposium 1, Geology and quality of life: Internat. Geol. Cong., 24th, Montreal, Canada 1972, p. 7–14.

Duncan, D. B., 1955, Multiple range and multiple F tests: Biometrics, v. 11, no. 4, p. 1–42.

Krumbein, W. C., and Slack, H. A., 1956, Statistical analysis of low-level radioactivity of Pennsylvanian black fissile shale in Illinois: Geol. Soc. America Bull., v. 67, no. 6, p. 739–762.

McCloskey, P. N., 1971, Politics and the environment: Geol. Soc. America, Abs. with Programs, v. 3, no. 7, p. 643.

Miesch, A. T., 1967, Theory of error in geochemical data: U.S. Geol. Survey Prof. Paper 574–A, 17 p.

Shacklette, H. T., Erdman, J. A., and Keith, J. R., 1970, Geochemical survey of vegetation, in Geochemical survey of Missouri, plans and progress for second six-month period (January–June 1970): U.S. Geol. Survey Open-File Rept., p. 36–47.

——1971, Geochemical survey of vegetation, in Geochemical survey of Missouri, plans and progress for fourth six-month period (January–June 1971): U.S. Geol. Survey Open-File Rept., p. 27–46.

——1972, Geochemical survey of vegetation, in Geochemical survey of Missouri, plans and progress for fifth six-month period (July–December 1971): U.S. Geol. Survey Open-File Rept., p. 56–98.

U.S. Geological Survey, 1969, Geochemical survey of Missouri, plans and progress for first six-month period (July–December 1969): U.S. Geol. Survey Open-File Rept., 49 p.

Youden, W. J., and Mehlich, A., 1937, Selection of efficient methods for soil sampling: Boyce Thompson Inst. Contr., v. 9, p. 59–70.

PAPER PRESENTED AT THE 1972 ANNUAL MEETING OF THE GEOLOGICAL SOCIETY OF AMERICA IN MINNEAPOLIS, MINNESOTA

MANUSCRIPT RECEIVED BY THE SOCIETY SEPTEMBER 17, 1973

THE
GEOLOGICAL SOCIETY
OF AMERICA